How to use your *Flip Quiz*

If you are answering questions on your own, just cover the answers with your hand or a piece of card. You may want to write down your answers and count up your scores for each quiz.

If you are doing the quizzes with a partner or in teams, unfold the base and stand the *Flip Quiz* on a flat surface between you and your partner. Read aloud the questions (but not the answers!) and allow your partner to say the answers or write them down.

You may answer each question in turn or answer an entire quiz in turn. Keep your scores on a piece of paper and compare results.

The illustrations are there to help you get the right answers when competing with a partner. For instance, if you are answering Quiz 1 questions, you will be looking at and reading out Quiz 2. However, the images you will see are clues to help you with Quiz 1. The labels next to the illustrations tell you which question they are clues for.

The questions are divided into nine subjects: General Knowledge, TV and Film, Food and Drink, the Natural World, Sport, Geography, History, Science and Maths, and the Bible.

Categories
Choose which category you would like to answer questions on – you have a choice of nine

Questions
Each quiz is made up of ten questions

Answers
When doing the quizzes on your own, cover the answers with your hand or a piece of card

Picture clues
These visual clues will often help you get the answer – the label tells you which question they refer to

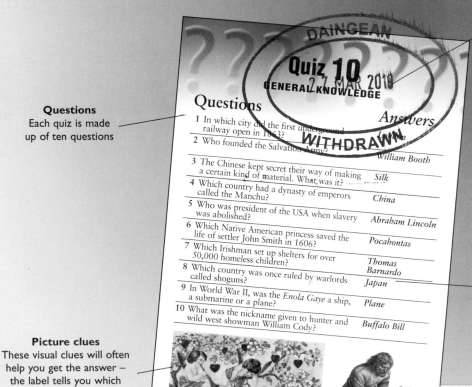

DAINGEAN

Quiz 10
27 MAR 2010
GENERAL KNOWLEDGE

Questions

Answers

WITHDRAWN

1 In which city did the first underground railway open in 1863?

2 Who founded the Salvation Army?
William Booth

3 The Chinese kept secret their way of making a certain kind of material. What was it?
Silk

4 Which country had a dynasty of emperors called the Manchu?
China

5 Who was president of the USA when slavery was abolished?
Abraham Lincoln

6 Which Native American princess saved the life of settler John Smith in 1606?
Pocahontas

7 Which Irishman set up shelters for over 50,000 homeless children?
Thomas Barnardo

8 Which country was once ruled by warlords called shoguns?
Japan

9 In World War II, was the *Enola Gaye* a ship, a submarine or a plane?
Plane

10 What was the nickname given to hunter and wild west showman William Cody?
Buffalo Bill

Quiz 9
Question 4

Quiz 9
Question 5

Quiz 1
GENERAL KNOWLEDGE

Questions	Answers
1 Which country developed the Space Shuttle?	*The USA*
2 What breed of dog is Beethoven in the 1992 movie?	*St Bernard*
3 Who was the most famous escape artist of the 20th century?	*Harry Houdini*
4 What did Alexander Graham Bell invent in 1877?	*The telephone*
5 In which century did people first travel in cars?	*19th century*
6 What machine did James Hargreaves invent?	*The spinning jenny*
7 What did Volta invent in 1800?	*The electric battery*
8 Which English king was killed at the Battle of Bosworth in 1485?	*Richard III*
9 Which state in ancient Greece forced its people to live a strict life without any luxuries?	*Sparta*
10 In which sport did Jack Nicklaus find fame and fortune?	*Golf*

Quiz 2
Question 4

Quiz 2
Question 8

Quiz 2
Question 3

Quiz 2
GENERAL KNOWLEDGE

Questions	Answers
1 Which bear is smarter than the average bear?	*Yogi Bear*
2 What was the painter Picasso's first name?	*Pablo*
3 Who was Queen of England at the time of the Spanish Armada?	*Elizabeth I*
4 What kind of warplane is a B-52?	*A long-range bomber*
5 Which fast food gets its name from a city in Germany?	*Hamburger (from Hamburg)*
6 Of which revolution was Robespierre a leader?	*The French Revolution*
7 Who was Robin Hood's sweetheart?	*Maid Marian*
8 What was a boneshaker?	*An early bicycle*
9 Who is the father of Britain's princes William and Harry?	*Charles, Prince of Wales*
10 What bird is depicted on the coat of arms of the USA?	*Bald eagle*

Quiz I
Question 10

Quiz I
Question 2

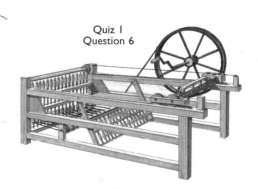

Quiz I
Question 6

Quiz 3
SCIENCE AND MATHS

Questions	Answers
1 What does REM stand for with regard to sleep patterns?	*Rapid Eye Movement*
2 Which planet is closest to the Sun?	*Mercury*
3 H is the chemical symbol of which gas?	*Hydrogen*
4 The shape of a rainbow is a circle. True or false?	*True*
5 Incisors and canines are both types of what?	*Teeth*
6 Is your heart above or below your stomach?	*Above*
7 What is meteorology the study of?	*Weather*
8 How many corners does a rectangle have?	*Four*
9 What is the name for a boat that travels underwater?	*Submarine*
10 How many fives are there in 45?	*Nine*

Quiz 4
Question 7

Quiz 4
Question 10

Quiz 4

SCIENCE AND MATHS

Questions	Answers
1 What is the cube root of nine?	*Three*
2 Do we hear thunder or see lightning first?	*See lightning*
3 What is the name of the part of the eye that surrounds the pupil?	*Iris*
4 Over half the human body comprises of what?	*Water*
5 What is the main acid constituent of acid rain?	*Sulphuric acid*
6 What name is given to a triangle that has three equal sides and three equal angles?	*Equilateral*
7 What device powers a torch?	*Battery*
8 How many hours are there in a day?	24
9 What are dairy products made from?	*Milk*
10 Which toy is the oldest flying machine?	*Kite*

Quiz 3
Question 6

Quiz 3
Question 9

Quiz 5
GENERAL KNOWLEDGE

Questions	Answers
1 Who painted the *Mona Lisa*?	*Leonardo da Vinci*
2 Was the Mustang a famous fighter plane or a kind of gun?	*US fighter plane*
3 Who travelled non-stop around the world in a balloon in 1999?	*Brian James and Bertrand Picard*
4 Which English king had six wives?	*Henry VIII*
5 Who in the Bible lost his strength when his hair was cut?	*Samson*
6 Which famous explorer was killed in Hawaii in 1779?	*Captain James Cook*
7 What was the first antibiotic drug?	*Penicillin*
8 In which country is El Cid a national hero?	*Spain*
9 Which of the Seven Wonders of the Ancient World was in the city of Babylon?	*The Hanging Gardens*
10 How many lanes are there in an Olympic swimming pool?	*Eight*

Quiz 6
Question 4

Quiz 6
Question 2

Quiz 6
GENERAL KNOWLEDGE

Questions	Answers
1 At which battle did the Sioux defeat General Custer?	*Battle of the Little Big Horn*
2 Which famous Italian leader had a biscuit named after him?	*Guiseppe Garibaldi*
3 Which African city is overlooked by Table Mountain?	*Cape Town*
4 Which animal inspired Robert the Bruce of Scotland to try again?	*Spider*
5 Which tramp with a bowler hat and cane was much-loved by silent movie-goers?	*Charlie Chaplin*
6 What animal gave milk to the twins Romulus and Remus when they were left to die?	*She-wolf*
7 Published in 2005, what is the title of the sixth Harry Potter novel?	Harry Potter and the Half Blood Prince
8 For what occupation was Jesus trained?	*Carpentry*
9 In which war was the Battle of the Somme?	*World War I (1914–1918)*
10 Did Sir Francis Chichester fly or sail around the world?	*He sailed around the world in 1967*

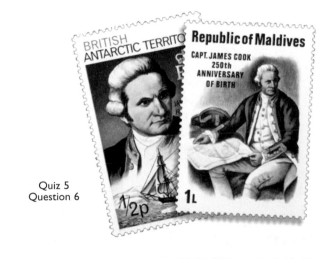

Quiz 5
Question 6

Quiz 5
Question 4

Quiz 7

NATURAL WORLD

Questions	Answers
1 Which prickly mammal curls into a ball when alarmed?	*Hedgehog*
2 What type of animal is Kaa in *The Jungle Book*?	*Snake*
3 Is a pondskater a fish, a frog or an insect?	*Insect*
4 Which bird hunts at night – the owl or hawk?	*Owl*
5 A gosling is the young of which bird?	*Goose*
6 Do herons dive for fish or catch them in the shallows?	*Catch them in the shallows*
7 Which tree-dwelling animal has a home called a drey?	*Squirrel*
8 What animal's name can go before hound, glove and trot?	*Fox*
9 Did woolly mammoths resemble elephants or bears?	*Elephants*
10 Which mammal's name is also one of the seven deadly sins?	*Sloth*

Quiz 8
Question 5

Quiz 8
Question 2

Quiz 8
NATURAL WORLD

Questions	Answers
1 What colour is a raven?	Black
2 What are the biggest spiders?	Tarantulas
3 What does a cygnet grow into?	Swan
4 If herbivore equals vegetable, what word equates to meat?	Carnivore
5 What is a ladyslipper – a plant or an insect?	Plant
6 Which animal gives birth to the largest young?	Blue whale
7 A drone is the male of which winged creature?	Bee
8 Which marsupial is depicted on the Australian coat of arms?	Kangaroo
9 What is the world's largest cat?	Tiger
10 Do apes or monkeys have tails?	Monkeys

Quiz 7
Question 2

Quiz 7
Question 4

Quiz 9
GENERAL KNOWLEDGE

Questions	Answers
1 Who crossed Niagara Falls on a tightrope in 1859?	*Charles Blondin*
2 Which is the largest of the Great Lakes in North America?	*Lake Superior*
3 Which nationality of people founded the Ottoman Empire?	*Turkish*
4 Which Daniel Defoe character spent 24 years marooned on a desert island?	*Robinson Crusoe*
5 In Greek mythology Eros was the god of what?	*Love*
6 By what name was writer Charles Lutwidge Dodgson better known?	*Lewis Carroll*
7 What is the underground railway system in Paris called?	*The Metro*
8 Are Jesuit priests Roman Catholic or Protestant?	*Roman Catholic*
9 Which country was invaded on D-Day in 1944?	*France*
10 What sport takes place in a velodrome?	*Cycling*

Quiz 10
Question 10

Quiz 10
Question 6

Quiz 10

GENERAL KNOWLEDGE

Questions	Answers
1 In which city did the first underground railway open in 1863?	*London*
2 Who founded the Salvation Army?	*William Booth*
3 The Chinese kept secret their way of making a certain kind of material. What was it?	*Silk*
4 Which country had a dynasty of emperors called the Manchu?	*China*
5 Who was president of the USA when slavery was abolished?	*Abraham Lincoln*
6 Which Native American princess saved the life of settler John Smith in 1606?	*Pocahontas*
7 Which Irishman set up shelters for over 50,000 homeless children?	*Thomas Barnardo*
8 Which country was once ruled by warlords called shoguns?	*Japan*
9 In World War II, was the *Enola Gaye* a ship, a submarine or a plane?	*Plane*
10 What was the nickname given to hunter and wild west showman William Cody?	*Buffalo Bill*

Quiz 9
Question 4

Quiz 9
Question 5

Quiz 11
GEOGRAPHY

Questions	Answers
1 What is the world's largest gulf?	*Gulf of Mexico*
2 What is the capital of Thailand?	*Bangkok*
3 Which animal is most commonly farmed for its meat in the Falkland Islands?	*Sheep*
4 What is the state fruit of Georgia, USA?	*Peach*
5 Which famous art museum is in Paris?	*The Louvre*
6 Does the potato grow above or below ground?	*Below ground*
7 Which is the world's most highly populated continent?	*Asia*
8 Aberdeen Angus and Jersey are breeds of which farm animal?	*Cow*
9 Quantas is an airline in which country?	*Australia*
10 In what continent would you find the mountain range called the Andes?	*South America*

Quiz 12
Question 1

Quiz 12
Question 2

Quiz 12
GEOGRAPHY

Questions	Answers
1 In which country is the popular holiday destination of Eilat?	Israel
2 Which primates are only found in Madagascar and the Comoros Islands?	Lemurs
3 In which South American country was the lost city of the Incas discovered in 1911?	Peru
4 Which was the first country to employ the metric system?	France
5 In which country was Lego invented?	Denmark
6 Gorgonzola cheese was named after a town in which country?	Italy
7 What became the 50th state of the USA in 1959?	Hawaii
8 Is the Indian Ocean bigger or smaller than the Antarctic Ocean?	Bigger
9 Which sea separates Europe from North Africa?	Mediterranean
10 The Grand Canyon is found in which country?	USA

Quiz 11
Question 5

Quiz 13
GENERAL KNOWLEDGE

Questions	Answers
1 On which continent did Henry Morton Stanley meet Dr David Livingstone?	*Africa*
2 Which country did Germany invade in September 1939?	*Poland*
3 What four-letter B word is the collective name for a group of asteroids?	*Belt*
4 Who was the first woman in space in 1963?	*Valentina Tereshkova*
5 With what invention is the name of Gillette associated?	*Safety razor*
6 The Northrop f-5 'Freedom fighter' saw service in which war: World War II or the Vietnam War?	*Vietnam War*
7 What was the name of the giant statue that once stood at the entrance of Rhodes harbour?	*Colossus*
8 Which city won the vote to host the 2012 Summer Olympics?	*London*
9 Which bridge was opened to the public of San Francisco in 1937?	*Golden Gate Bridge*
10 What medical first did Christiaan Barnard of South Africa achieve in 1967?	*First heart transplant*

Quiz 14
Question 10

Quiz 14
Question 9

Quiz 14

Questions

Answers

1 In which river was Jesus baptized?
River Jordan

2 Which Greek hero could only be wounded in his heels?
Achilles

3 In which war was radar first used?
World War II (1939–1945)

4 What was the name of the Scottish hero in the film *Braveheart*?
William Wallace

5 In which Indian city did Mother Teresa carry out her good works?
Calcutta

6 Which Christian saint is famous for his love of animals?
St Francis of Assisi

7 Which gem is traditionally January's birthstone?
Garnet

8 Which land did Cartier claim for France in 1534?
Canada

9 Which of Henry VIII's wives was the mother of Elizabeth I?
Anne Boleyn

10 Which Egyptian pharaoh's tomb was discovered in 1922?
Tutankhamun

Quiz 13
Question 6

Quiz 15
HISTORY

Questions	Answers
1 How many years does a term of a US president last?	*Four*
2 Which explorer was first to reach the South Pole?	*Roald Amundsen*
3 What is an abacus used for?	*Mathematical calculations*
4 What A word is the Spanish for navy?	*Armada*
5 Which country used to be led by rulers called tsars?	*Russia*
6 In which foreign wars did King Richard I of England go to fight?	*The Crusades*
7 What do we call the ancient form of decoration using small pieces of tile or stone?	*Mosaic*
8 Fletcher Christian led an infamous mutiny on which ship?	**The Bounty**
9 The first ever Roman emperor gave his name to which month of the year?	*August (Augustine)*
10 What event do the French celebrate on 14 July?	*The fall of the Bastille*

Quiz 16
Question 3

Quiz 16
Question 2

Quiz 16
HISTORY

Questions	Answers
1 Which began first: the French Revolution or the American Revolution?	*American (in 1775)*
2 How many wheels did a Celtic war chariot have?	*Two*
3 What kind of boats did Polynesians use for ocean voyages?	*Outrigger canoes*
4 Which Greek philosopher lived in a barrel?	*Diogenes*
5 Of which people was Genghis Khan a war leader?	*The Mongols*
6 In Shakespeare's play, who does Juliet fall in love with?	*Romeo*
7 In which country did the ancient Olmecs live?	*Mexico*
8 In which war did American troops defeat English troops at the Battle of Yorktown?	*American War of Independence*
9 Which US city was originally called New Amsterdam?	*New York*
10 After which Greek victory did a messenger run 42 km to announce the good news?	*Marathon in 490BC*

Quiz 15
Question 4

Quiz 15
Question 2

Quiz 17
GENERAL KNOWLEDGE

Questions	Answers
1 Which musical instrument is associated with Yehudi Menuhin?	*Violin*
2 What were the forenames of Laurel and Hardy?	*Stanley and Oliver*
3 Why did the *Titanic* sink?	*It hit an iceberg*
4 America was the New World: where was the Old World?	*Europe and Asia*
5 In which film did Oliver Reed make his screen farewell?	*Gladiator*
6 What is the oldest state of the USA?	*Delaware*
7 Who wrote about a hedgehog called Mrs Tiggywinkle?	*Beatrix Potter*
8 What nationality was Alexander Graham Bell, inventor of the telephone?	*Scottish*
9 Who led the Argonauts on their search for the Golden Fleece?	*Jason*
10 Which war was fought between the Union and the Confederacy?	*American Civil War*

Quiz 18
Question 10

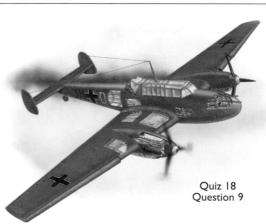

Quiz 18
Question 9

Quiz 18
GENERAL KNOWLEDGE

Questions	Answers
1 What does E stand for in Einstein's famous equation E=mc²?	*Energy*
2 Who painted the ceiling of the Sistine Chapel in Rome?	*Michelangelo*
3 What was used to execute people during the French Revolution's 'Reign of Terror'?	*Guillotine*
4 By what name was Zimbabwe previously known?	*Rhodesia*
5 In the Bible, Moses parted the waves of which sea?	*Red Sea*
6 Which of the nine planets is symbolized by a trident?	*Neptune*
7 Which murderer terrorized part of London in 1888?	*Jack the Ripper*
8 Which war began after the assassination of Archduke Ferdinand in Sarajevo?	*World War I*
9 In World War II, what was a Messerschmitt ME-110?	*German bomber plane*
10 What was the name of the highly trained killers of feudal Japan?	*Ninjas*

Quiz 17
Question 5

Quiz 17
Question 7

Quiz 19

SCIENCE AND MATHS

Questions	Answers
1 What is measured in litres and millilitres?	*Liquid*
2 What is the more common name for the olfactory organ?	*Nose*
3 What covers more of the Earth: land or sea?	*Sea*
4 Which numbers show on a digital clock at midnight?	*00:00*
5 What is formed when a river flows over a cliff?	*Waterfall*
6 What is the lightest gas?	*Hydrogen*
7 What kind of energy flows along wires into homes?	*Electricity*
8 Which of these shapes would not roll – cylinder, sphere or cuboid?	*Cuboid*
9 What does the E stand for in email?	*Electronic*
10 What vehicle rushes people to hospital in an emergency?	*Ambulance*

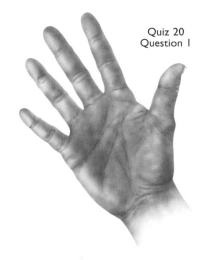

Quiz 20
Question 1

Quiz 20
Question 8

Quiz 20

SCIENCE AND MATHS

Questions	Answers
1 Where in the human body is the Mount of Venus?	*Palm of the hand*
2 What food is made from cocoa beans?	*Chocolate*
3 Where are the quadriceps muscles located?	*Thigh*
4 What N is the top number of a fraction?	*Numerator*
5 What is the next prime number after seven?	*11*
6 What is the chemical symbol of ice?	H_2O
7 What is the middle colour of a rainbow?	*Green*
8 Horology is the science or study of what?	*Time*
9 How many degrees are there in a semi-circle?	*180*
10 What B is the name given to the study of projectiles?	*Ballistics*

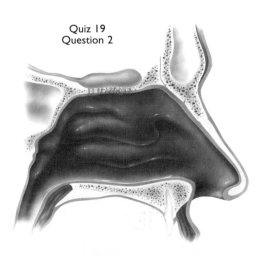

Quiz 19
Question 2

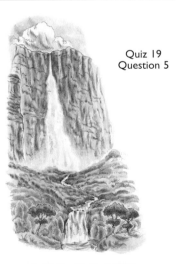

Quiz 19
Question 5

Quiz 21

GENERAL KNOWLEDGE

Questions	Answers
1 In the War of American Independence, which country joined in on America's side in 1779?	*Spain*
2 Which country was Menachem Begin leader of in the 1970s?	*Israel*
3 In which war did Robert E Lee surrender to Ulysses S Grant?	*American Civil War*
4 Of which African country was Idi Amin the dictator?	*Uganda*
5 Which hated queen of France was executed in 1793?	*Marie Antoinette*
6 What did Jethro Tull invent in the 18th century?	*Seed drill*
7 Who painted *The Scream*?	*Edvard Munch*
8 Which religion has its centre at the Golden Temple in Amritsar, India?	*Sikhism*
9 Which big country was named by mistake after the Native American word for 'village'?	*Canada*
10 What nationality was psychoanalyst Sigmund Freud?	*Austrian*

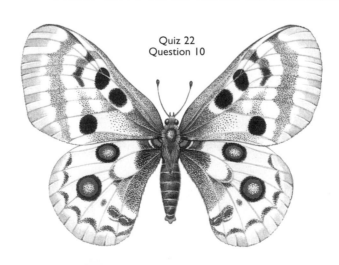

Quiz 22
Question 10

Quiz 22

GENERAL KNOWLEDGE

Questions	Answers
1 What radioactive element was discovered by Pierre and Marie Curie?	*Radium*
2 What African warriors fought in groups called impis?	*Zulus*
3 What was the name of the 'land of milk and honey' where Abraham led the Israelites?	*Canaan*
4 What invention by Elisha Otis in 1854 made it easier to live in skyscrapers?	*Elevator*
5 What kind of animal was the 18th-century artist George Stubbs famous for painting?	*The horse*
6 Which Stuart king ruled from 1488 to 1513?	*James IV of Scotland*
7 Who is the patron saint of dancers?	*St Vitus*
8 Where, in ancient Greek myth, was the River Styx?	*The Underworld*
9 Who wrote *Kidnapped*?	*Robert Louis Stevenson*
10 Which swimming stroke made its Olympic debut in 1956?	*Butterfly*

Quiz 21
Question 6

Questions	Answers
1 Are ET's eyes green, blue, brown or yellow?	*Blue*
2 What is the name of Homer Simpson's youngest daughter?	*Maggie*
3 Which animated superhero does Bob Parr transform into when donning a red suit?	*Mr Incredible*
4 What kind of animal is Rocky in *The Adventures of Rocky and Bullwinkle*?	*Squirrel*
5 Which film features the characters of Fred, Velma, Daphne, Shaggy and a talking dog?	Scooby-Doo
6 What is the name of the piggybank in *Toy Story*?	*Hamm*
7 Which 2000 animated film sees Emperor Kuzco transformed into a llama?	**The Emperor's New Groove**
8 In the film *Dinosaur* what is the name of the leader of the dinosaurs?	*Kron*
9 Is the family cat in the film *Stuart Little,* black, white or tortoiseshell?	*White*
10 In which film is Bugs Bunny assisted by basketball superstar Michael Jordan?	**Space Jam**

Quiz 24
Question 5

Questions	Answers
1 In which film does a sheep dog called Fly become a foster parent to a pig?	**Babe**
2 Which feline character is voiced by Antonio Banderas in *Shrek 2*?	***Puss in Boots***
3 Who stole Christmas in a 2000 film?	***The Grinch***
4 In the film *Johnny Neutron*, what piece of kitchen equipment is made into a satellite?	***Toaster***
5 What kind of animal is Bullwinkle in *The Adventures of Rocky and Bullwinkle*?	***Moose***
6 What is the name of Sid's dog in *Toy Story*?	***Scud***
7 Which film features a hen called Ginger and farm owners called Mr and Mrs Tweedy?	**Chicken Run**
8 In the film *A Bug's Life*, Flik hires circus performers to defend his colony from what?	***Grasshoppers***
9 Manfred, Sid and Diego are all characters in which film?	**Ice Age**
10 What is the name of the bear who befriends Mowgli in *The Jungle Book*?	***Baloo***

Quiz 23
Question 9

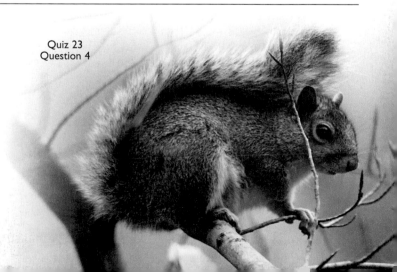

Quiz 23
Question 4

Quiz 25
GENERAL KNOWLEDGE

Questions	Answers
1 In Greek mythology, what was the huge monster with nine heads?	*The Hydra*
2 How many tarsal bones are there in a human's foot?	*Seven*
3 In the fairy story *Jack and the Beanstalk*, what animal did Jack exchange for a few beans?	*Cow*
4 Peter Parker is the secret identity of which superhero?	*Spiderman*
5 Pharaohs were ancient rulers in which country?	*Egypt*
6 In French, is *le soir*, morning or evening?	*Evening*
7 Which Russian cosmonaut became the first man in space in 1961?	*Yuri Gagarin*
8 What is the adopted name of US boxer Cassius Clay?	*Mohammed Ali*
9 What fruits are dried to make prunes?	*Plums*
10 In 2005 who sailed around the world in 71 days?	*Ellen MacArthur*

Quiz 26
Question 2

Quiz 26
Question 9

Quiz 26

GENERAL KNOWLEDGE

Questions	Answers
1 Where did the sauce used in the dish spaghetti bolognese originate?	*Bologna, Italy*
2 What four-letter word can go before step, bell and man?	*Door*
3 What kind of food is gazpacho?	*Soup*
4 Acorns are the fruits of which tree?	*Oak*
5 During World War II, what were U-boats?	*Submarines*
6 In computer terminology what does RAM stand for?	*Random Access Memory*
7 What vegetable does Bugs Bunny like best of all?	*Carrots*
8 What boy's name is an alternative name for an Academy Award?	*Oscar*
9 In which sport is 180 the highest achievable score with three throws?	*Darts*
10 Who did Cain kill in the first book of the Bible?	*Abel*

Quiz 25
Question 9

Quiz 27
NATURAL WORLD

Questions	Answers
1 What animal does the adjective equine relate to?	*Horse*
2 Does the rattlesnake rattle its head or its tail?	*Tail*
3 From which farm animal is Morocco leather obtained?	*Goat*
4 Which mammal is protected by sharp quills?	*Porcupine*
5 Do cones grow on pine trees or ash trees?	*Pine trees*
6 Is a seahorse a mammal or a fish?	*Fish*
7 Why is the leopard tortoise so-named?	*Its shell has spots like a leopard*
8 What colour does a chameleon's skin change to when angry?	*Black*
9 Which male big cat has a heavy mane on its neck and shoulders?	*Lion*
10 Is the red admiral a butterfly or moth?	*Butterfly*

Quiz 28
Question 5

Quiz 28
Question 6

Quiz 28
Question 3

Quiz 28
NATURAL WORLD

Questions	Answers
1 Do herrings swim alone or in shoals?	*Shoals*
2 Which bird lays the largest egg?	*Ostrich*
3 Which sea creature usually has five limbs?	*Starfish*
4 What name is given to a baby elephant?	*Calf*
5 Which edible bulb of the onion family is, according to legend, a vampire repellent?	*Garlic*
6 What is a scarlet macaw – a bird or a butterfly?	*Bird*
7 What kind of animal is a snake?	*Reptile*
8 Does an octopus have teeth or a beak?	*Beak*
9 What kind of animal is an ocelot?	*Wild cat*
10 Which boy's name is also the home of a rabbit?	*Warren*

Quiz 27
Question 7

Quiz 27
Question 9

Quiz 27
Question 1

Quiz 29
GENERAL KNOWLEDGE

Questions	Answers
1 What three colours are depicted on the flag of Belgium?	*Yellow, black and red*
2 What grew in length when the puppet boy Pinocchio told lies?	*His nose*
3 According to the well-known proverb, what begins at home?	*Charity*
4 What is the more common name of the capsicum?	*Red pepper*
5 Which shark is named after the shape of its head and a DIY tool?	*Hammerhead shark*
6 In the nursery rhyme, which bells said 'You owe me five farthings'?	*The bells of St Martin's*
7 From what wood are baseball bats traditionally made?	*Ash*
8 What is the most highly populated city in the state of Alaska?	*Anchorage*
9 Who was the first woman mentioned in the Bible?	*Eve*
10 What is a basilisk?	*Lizard*

Quiz 30
Question 8

Quiz 30
Question 3

Quiz 30

GENERAL KNOWLEDGE

Questions	Answers
1 Name the biblical father of Shem, Ham and Japeth who built a vessel from gopher wood.	*Noah*
2 On which Mediterranean island was Napoleon Bonaparte born?	*Corsica*
3 Which saint's day is celebrated in Ireland on March 17?	*St Patrick*
4 What year witnessed the deaths of Princess Diana and Mother Teresa?	1997
5 What word can precede sick, weed and side?	*Sea*
6 Which N word is the name of the addictive substance found in tobacco?	*Nicotine*
7 Which famous painting was stolen from the Louvre in August 1911?	Mona Lisa
8 What type of creature is Beatrix Potter's character Jeremy Fisher?	*Frog*
9 Which of the seven dwarfs has the shortest name?	*Doc*
10 Who left Krypton, lived in Smallville, then gained employment in Metropolis?	*Superman*

Quiz 29
Question 4

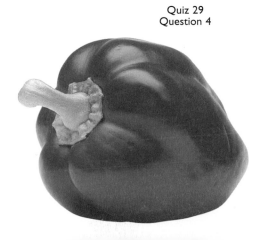

Quiz 31
SCIENCE AND MATHS

Questions	Answers
1 How many grams in half a kilogram?	500
2 How many sides does a hexagon have?	Six
3 What part of the body does the skull protect?	Brain
4 What does the Richter Scale measure?	Earthquakes
5 Which organ pumps blood around the body?	Heart
6 Which part of a car engine conducts heat away from the engine?	Radiator
7 Which of the nine planets is known as the Red Planet?	Mars
8 In 1783, what kind of aircraft carried the first air passengers?	Balloon
9 What are there 26 of in the human body?	Vertebrae
10 Which element was named after the planet Pluto?	Plutonium

Quiz 32
Question 3

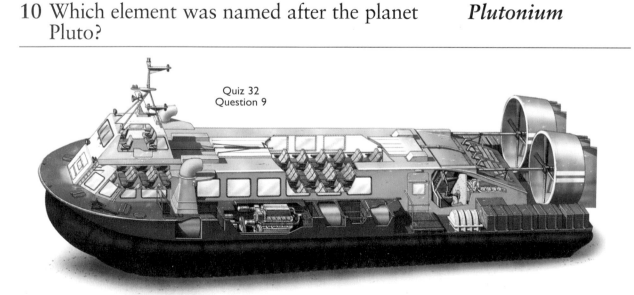

Quiz 32
Question 9

Quiz 32
SCIENCE AND MATHS

Questions	Answers
1 What total is obtained when adding together the sides of a pentagon and a triangle?	*Eight*
2 Why does an astronaut need to carry oxygen?	*Because there is no air in space*
3 What is the more common name for the patella, located in the leg?	*Kneecap*
4 What does an architect design?	*Buildings*
5 What has the most chromosomes, a chimpanzee or a human?	*Chimpanzee*
6 On which scale does a hurricane measure 12?	*Beaufort Scale*
7 In which code is the letter E represented by one dot?	*Morse Code*
8 Which of these materials is waterproof: wool, plastic or cotton?	*Plastic*
9 What kind of boat floats along on a cushion of air?	*Hovercraft*
10 What is zoophobia the fear of?	*Animals*

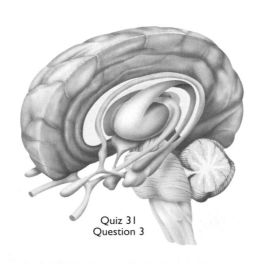

Quiz 31
Question 3

Quiz 31
Question 8

Quiz 33
GENERAL KNOWLEDGE

Questions	Answers
1 In *The Jungle Book*, what colour is Bagheera?	Black (a black panther)
2 Which gas is an anagram of the word none?	Neon
3 What word can precede print, bottle and bell?	Blue
4 Where did the Lost Boys live in the story of *Peter Pan*?	Neverland
5 Which country hosted the first Commonwealth Games?	Canada
6 The title of the French national anthem was inspired by which city?	Marseille
7 Was *Harry Potter and the Philosopher's Stone* the first book in the Harry Potter series?	Yes
8 What do the initials NFL stand for with regard to a sporting organization in the USA?	National Football League
9 Which literary doctor created *The Cat In The Hat*?	Dr Seuss
10 Who passes sentence at a court of law?	The judge

Quiz 34
Question 2

Quiz 34
Question 7

Quiz 34
MUSIC

Questions	Answers
1 How many strings does a violin have?	*Four*
2 What instrument is often called a squeeze box?	*Accordion*
3 What was the title of the Spice Girls' first UK No. 1 hit?	*"Wannabe"*
4 What is the last name of the singing sisters Dannii and Kylie?	*Minogue*
5 Which singer and actress sometimes abbreviates her name to J-Lo?	*Jennifer Lopez*
6 In the video for the Robbie Williams hit "Angels", does he ride a horse or motorbike?	*Motorbike*
7 In his hit record, what did Boy George sing after repeating the word karma five times?	*Chameleon*
8 What animated film about a green ogre climaxes with a karaoke session?	Shrek
9 What is the first name of John Travolta's character in *Grease*?	*Danny (Zuko)*
10 Are cymbals a percussion or brass instrument?	*Percussion*

Quiz 33
Question 2

Quiz 35
GEOGRAPHY

Questions	Answers
1 Is Greenland north or south of the Equator?	*North*
2 In which Australian city is Bondi Beach?	*Sydney*
3 Which country is famous for its fjords?	*Norway*
4 What is the second most highly populated city in the USA?	*Los Angeles*
5 The state capital of Arizona shares its name with which mythical bird?	*Phoenix*
6 On which continent are zebras found?	*Africa*
7 Which of these Caribbean islands is the largest: Haiti, Cuba or Jamaica?	*Cuba*
8 What is the flat Italian dough-based dish called?	*Pizza*
9 From which language does the word 'balcony' originate?	*Italian*
10 What were the feudal knights of Japan known as?	*Samurai*

Quiz 36
Question 8

Quiz 36
GEOGRAPHY

Questions	Answers
1 California has a large area of land set aside as a poppy flower reserve: true or false?	*True*
2 If you live in a rural environment, is your home in the town or countryside?	*Countryside*
3 Which Canadian city is the second largest French-speaking city in the world?	*Montreal*
4 What are the remote areas of Australia's interior known as?	*The outback*
5 Which canal provides an easier passage between the Atlantic and Pacific Oceans?	*Panama Canal*
6 What colour is the circle on the flag of Bangladesh?	*Red*
7 What is the world's largest bay?	*Hudson Bay*
8 What type of habitat is the Sahara?	*Desert*
9 In what country would you find the roads called autobahns?	*Germany*
10 Is Spain north or south of France?	*South*

Quiz 35
Question 10

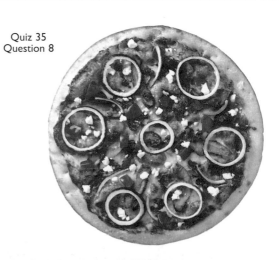

Quiz 35
Question 8

Quiz 37
TV AND FILM

Questions	Answers
1 Which sport was featured in the films *The Natural* and *A League of Their Own*?	*Baseball*
2 In which 2005 film does Nicole Kidman play a witch?	**Bewitched**
3 How are Mr Fantastic, the Invisible Girl, the Human Torch and The Thing collectively known?	*The Fantastic Four*
4 Which 2004 film saw Tom Hanks stranded at JFK Airport?	**The Terminal**
5 Which diminutive lord was voiced by John Lithgow in *Shrek*?	*Lord Farquaad*
6 In which 2005 film does Christian Bale play Bruce Wayne?	**Batman Begins**
7 What type of creature is Willy in the *Free Willy* films?	*Killer whale*
8 Who played Jack Dawson in *Titanic*?	*Leonardo DiCaprio*
9 In which city is the TV comedy *Friends* set?	*New York*
10 What colour is Marge Simpson's hair?	*Blue*

Quiz 38
Question 2

Quiz 38
Question 9

Quiz 38
SPORT

Questions	Answers
1 In which sport do England and Australia compete to win The Ashes?	*Cricket*
2 Ralf and Michael Schumacher are famous names in which sport?	*Motor racing*
3 In which athletics event did Dick Fosbury introduce a radical technique in 1968?	*High jump*
4 What are halyards used for?	*Hoisting sails*
5 How many minutes is a round in boxing?	*Three*
6 On a chessboard, what piece is also a member of the clergy?	*Bishop*
7 Which golfer won the British Open in 2005?	*Tiger Woods*
8 What do the initials SB indicate in baseball?	*Stolen base*
9 In which of the following sports is a volley not allowed: tennis, table tennis or badminton?	*Table tennis*
10 Which golf trophy did Europe win for the first time in 28 years in 1985?	*Ryder Cup*

Quiz 37
Question 7

Quiz 37
Question 1

Quiz 39
THE BIBLE

Questions	Answers
1 Why did Jairus ask Jesus for help?	*His daughter was very ill*
2 Who said, "Am I my brother's keeper?"	*Cain*
3 What did Ezekiel see in his vision?	*A valley of dry bones*
4 Is Adam or Esau described as 'a hairy man'?	*Esau*
5 Which sea did the Israelites have to cross to get to the Promised Land?	*The Red Sea*
6 How did Joseph, the husband of Mary, earn his living?	*He was a carpenter*
7 Which disciple was nicknamed 'the Doubter'?	*Thomas*
8 In the parable, what happened to the house built on sand when it rained?	*It fell down*
9 How many books are there in the New Testament?	*27*
10 How did Jesus help Bartimaeus?	*He cured his blindness*

Quiz 40
Question 9

Quiz 40
THE BIBLE

Questions	Answers
1 What did God create last in the story of the Creation?	*Humans*
2 How long did the flood last?	*40 days and nights*
3 Who became leader when Moses died?	*Joshua*
4 What made the walls of Jericho fall down?	*Israelites marching around the walls*
5 Where in the Bible would you find 150 songs of praise?	*The Book of Psalms*
6 For how long was Jesus in the wilderness, being tempted by the devil?	*40 days and nights*
7 Who said, "Fear not for behold I bring you good tidings of great joy"?	*Angels telling of the birth of Jesus*
8 Who took the body of Jesus and buried it in a tomb cut out of the rock?	*Joseph of Arimathea*
9 What kind of crown did the soldiers put on Jesus' head when he was crucified?	*Crown of thorns*
10 Which of the disciples was called 'The Rock'?	*Simon-Peter*

Quiz 39
Question 3

Quiz 41
NATURAL WORLD

Questions	Answers
1 What animal is a cross between a mare and an ass?	*Mule*
2 Does a female walrus have tusks?	*Yes*
3 What is the plural of fungus?	*Fungi*
4 What name is given to a male horse or pony that is less than four years of age?	*Colt*
5 Is the stamen the male or female organ of a plant?	*Male*
6 What is the alternative three-letter name for a Tibetan ox?	*Yak*
7 Is a young seal called a kitten, a pup or a cub?	*Pup*
8 What is the only bird that possesses nostrils?	*Kiwi*
9 Do snakes have eyelids?	*No*
10 From which flowers is opium obtained?	*Poppies*

Quiz 42
Question 8

Quiz 42
Question 10

Quiz 42
NATURAL WORLD

Questions	Answers
1 Which bird, native to the island of Mauritius, became extinct in 1681?	Dodo
2 What is the national bird of India?	Peacock
3 From which animal is the meat venison obtained?	Deer
4 What B word is the name given to whale fat?	Blubber
5 How many stomachs does a cow have?	Four
6 What is the world's tallest bird?	Ostrich
7 What is stored in a camel's hump?	Fat
8 What shape are honeycomb cells in a beehive?	Hexagonal
9 What kind of leaves provide the staple diet of a silkworm?	Mulberry
10 A male pig and a male bear share the same name, what is it?	Boar

Quiz 41
Question 8

Quiz 41
Question 3

Quiz 43
SCIENCE AND MATHS

Questions	Answers
1 What name is given to the mixture of gases emitted from a car engine?	*Exhaust*
2 What is a monsoon?	*Very heavy rainstorm*
3 How many angles are equal in an isosceles triangle?	*Two*
4 You breathe air in through which two parts of the body?	*Mouth and nose*
5 What colour do you get if you mix red and blue?	*Purple*
6 What C word is defined as an assemblage or group of stars?	*Constellation*
7 On a 24-hour digital clock, what numbers show at 4 pm?	*16:00*
8 At what times of day can the sky become red?	*Sunrise and sunset*
9 What is the total of five 5s and ten 4s?	*65*
10 The artist Leonardo da Vinci invented a flying machine 500 years ago – true or false?	*True*

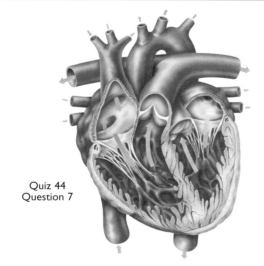

Quiz 44
Question 7

Quiz 44
Question 6

Quiz 44
SCIENCE AND MATHS

Questions	Answers
1 Which kind of clock measures time by the Sun?	*Sundial*
2 What is another name for perspiration?	*Sweat*
3 Name one of the four types of weather that could be described as precipitation?	*Hail, sleet, snow or rain*
4 Which numbers show on a digital clock at a quarter to 11 in the morning?	*10:45*
5 Where in the human body would you find the hammer and the anvil?	*Ear (bones)*
6 Which invention was first called a phonograph?	*Gramophone*
7 What part of the body works like a pump?	*Heart*
8 Nimbus and cumulus are both types of what?	*Clouds*
9 Mass multiplied by acceleration equals what F?	*Force*
10 What is a microchip made of?	*Silicon*

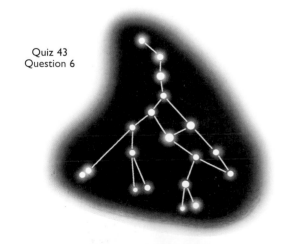

Quiz 43
Question 6

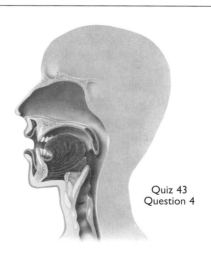

Quiz 43
Question 4

Quiz 45
HISTORY

Questions	Answers
1 What was the tax protest carried out in December 1773 in Massachusetts, USA?	*Boston Tea Party*
2 Which continent was Ernest Shackleton famous for exploring?	*Antarctica*
3 Which Norman king ordered the compilation of the Domesday Book?	*William the Conqueror*
4 What did Ladislao Biro invent in 1933?	*Ballpoint pen*
5 Which Texan city was named after the first President of the Republic of Texas?	*Houston*
6 Catherine II of Russia is better known as who?	*Catherine the Great*
7 What is named after the German physicist Hans Geiger?	*The Geiger Counter*
8 What did Peter Conrad become the third person to do, following Neil and Buzz?	*Walk on the Moon*
9 Baron Manfred von Richthofen or the Red Baron was a pilot during which war?	*World War I*
10 Which historical age preceded the Iron Age?	*The Bronze Age*

Quiz 46
Question 10

Quiz 46
Question 3

Quiz 46
HISTORY

Questions	Answers
1 In 1947, Chuck Yeager became the first pilot to break what?	*Sound barrier*
2 Which king did Sean Connery portray in the film *Robin Hood, Prince of Thieves*?	*Richard the Lionheart*
3 Name the Italian dictator who was known as Il Duce?	*Benito Mussolini*
4 In which war was the Battle of the Coral Sea contested?	*World War II*
5 Which US city acquired the nickname of the Alamo City?	*San Antonio*
6 Which Native American Indian tribe was led by Geronimo?	*Apache*
7 Named after a French king, what became the 18th state of the USA?	*Louisiana*
8 Where in London is the Bloody Tower?	*Tower of London*
9 In 1912, which ship became the first to use the newly adapted SOS distress signal?	**Titanic**
10 Davy Crockett's hat was made from the skin and fur of which animal?	*Raccoon*

Quiz 45
Question 7

Quiz 45
Question 3

Questions	Answers
1 Which owner of a chocolate factory did Charlie Bucket meet on screen?	*Willy Wonka*
2 Which cartoon film tells the story of a lost Russian princess?	**Anastasia**
3 Which American state shares its name with the first name of Dr Jones?	*Indiana*
4 What is the name of Tarzan's female companion?	*Jane*
5 What is the name of Disney's flying elephant?	*Dumbo*
6 Which capital city did the Rugrats venture to in a 2000 film?	*Paris*
7 What does the A stand for in the Steven Spielberg movie *AI*?	*Artificial*
8 What kind of animal is Maid Marian in Disney's cartoon version of *Robin Hood*?	*Fox*
9 What is the name of the young boy who is a close friend of Winnie the Pooh?	*Christopher Robin*
10 Which girl accompanied Peter Pan to Neverland?	*Wendy Darling*

Quiz 48
Question 3

Questions	Answers
1 In which country is the Disney film *Mulan* set?	*China*
2 What kind of creepy crawlies featured in the film *Arachnophobia*?	*Spiders*
3 What kind of dinosaur is the monster featured in the 1998 film *Godzilla*?	Tyrannosaurus Rex
4 What is the favourite food of the cartoon cat Garfield?	*Lasagne*
5 How many of the seven dwarfs have a name beginning with S?	*Two – Sleepy and Sneezy*
6 The Hood is the archenemy of which family in *Thunderbirds*?	*Tracy family*
7 What is the name of the bird that Stuart Little rescues from the clutches of a falcon?	*Margalo*
8 Which 1997 cartoon film features the characters of Pain, Panic and Pegasus?	Hercules
9 To which islands do the Spy Kids venture in their second film outing?	*Islands of Lost Dreams*
10 What is the name of Fred Flintstone's best friend?	*Barney Rubble*

Quiz 47
Question 1

Quiz 47
Question 8

Quiz 49
GENERAL KNOWLEDGE

Questions	Answers
1 Rat, red and tree are all species of which marsupial?	*Kangaroo*
2 Which villain was assisted by Muttley in the cartoon series *Wacky Races*?	*Dick Dastardly*
3 In which 1939 film did Charles Laughton play Quasimodo?	**The Hunchback of Notre Dame**
4 Soot consists mainly of which chemical element?	*Carbon*
5 Where was Elvis Presley crying according to a 1965 hit?	*In the chapel*
6 What are the tall twin towers in Kuala Lumpur called?	*The Petronas Towers*
7 What type of animal is Disney's Bambi?	*Deer*
8 Jasmine and long grain are both types of which foodstuff?	*Rice*
9 Who plays one half of Starsky and Hutch and also recorded the song "Silver Lady"?	*David Soul*
10 MO is the zip code for which state of the USA?	*Missouri*

Quiz 50
Question 10

Quiz 50
Question 7

Quiz 50
GENERAL KNOWLEDGE

Questions	Answers
1 By what other name is the heavenly body Sirius also known?	*The Dog Star*
2 The world record of which athletic event was held by Jesse Owens for 25 years?	*Long jump*
3 Traditionally, what is known as the Lower House in the US Congress?	*House of Representatives*
4 Which Australian city is to host the 2006 Commonwealth Games?	*Melbourne*
5 What is the name of Herman Munster's wife?	*Lily*
6 By what name is Gordon Sumner better known?	*Sting*
7 Siberian, Caspian and Bengal are species of which animal?	*Tiger*
8 What did Cape Kennedy change its name to?	*Cape Canaveral*
9 How was Lee Yuen Kam better known in the world of films?	*Bruce Lee*
10 What is an alternative name for a bison?	*Buffalo*

Quiz 49
Question 6

Quiz 49
Question 7

Quiz 49
Question 1

Quiz 51
TV AND FILM

Questions	Answers
1 Which role does Emma Watson play in the Harry Potter films?	*Hermione Granger*
2 In which TV drama does Kiefer Sutherland play the hero Jack Bauer?	**24**
3 Which sport features in the 2005 film *Coach Carter*?	*Basketball*
4 In which country are the battle scenes of *Saving Private Ryan* set?	*France*
5 The film *Master And Commander* was set during which war?	*Napoleonic War*
6 What is the name of Monica's brother in *Friends*?	*Ross*
7 Who appeared alongside her father Jon Voight in the film *Lara Croft: Tomb Raider*?	*Angelina Jolie*
8 Which 2002 film starring Tom Cruise is set in the year 2054?	**Minority Report**
9 In which film does a gang of children search for the treasure of 'One-Eyed' Willy?	**The Goonies**
10 Who does Anakin Skywalker transform into in *The Revenge of the Sith*?	*Darth Vader*

Quiz 52
Question 10

Quiz 52
TV AND FILM

Questions	Answers
1 Which 2005 film sees Tom Cruise fleeing an alien invasion?	War of the Worlds
2 What is Will's occupation in the US comedy series *Will and Grace*?	*Lawyer*
3 Which 2005 cartoon features four residents of Central Park zoo who are shipped back to Africa?	Madagascar
4 Whose funeral was broadcast live on TV around the world on 8 April, 2005?	*Pope John Paul II*
5 Which computer-animated film features a character called Rodney Copperbottom?	Robots
6 Which 1999 cartoon film is subtitled *Bigger, Longer and Uncut*?	South Park
7 In 2002, the first Oscar for Best Animation went to which film?	Shrek
8 Who provided the voice of Mickey Mouse in his cartoon debut?	*Walt Disney*
9 Who played Willie Wonka in a 2005 film?	*Johnny Depp*
10 Which film tells the story of a Hawaiian girl who adopts a dog that is disguised as an alien?	Lilo and Stitch

Quiz 51
Question 9

Quiz 53
GENERAL KNOWLEDGE

Questions	Answers
1 Which mountain range in Turkey bears the name of a sign of the zodiac?	*Taurus*
2 Which US president is depicted on a US $5 bill?	*Abraham Lincoln*
3 The Althing, the world's oldest parliament, governs which European country?	*Iceland*
4 Which US state is known as 'The Show Me' state and has Jefferson City as its capital?	*Missouri*
5 Which song contains the line 'If the sky that we look upon should tumble and fall'?	*"Stand By Me"*
6 What is the name for a triangular-shaped piece of land at the mouth of a river?	*Delta*
7 Was Chico or Groucho the eldest of the Marx Brothers?	*Chico*
8 Bert, Ernie and Big Bird all lived on which TV street?	*Sesame Street*
9 What is the country of origin of Darjeeling tea?	*India*
10 Which Hollywood star played the father of Courtney Cox in the sitcom *Friends*?	*Elliot Gould*

Quiz 54
Question 2

Quiz 54
Question 1

Quiz 54

GENERAL KNOWLEDGE

Questions	Answers
1 If you ordered *pollo* at an Italian restaurant, what would you be eating?	*Chicken*
2 A picture of which building is depicted on a US $20 bill?	*The White House*
3 Which cartoon character was originally called Happy Rabbit?	*Bugs Bunny*
4 What US state is nicknamed The Golden State and has a golden poppy as its state flower?	*California*
5 What fruity first name did Gwyneth Paltrow give to her daughter, born in 2004?	*Apple*
6 Which song opens with the words 'Goodbye Norma Jean'?	*"Candle In The Wind"*
7 Which French actress, nicknamed The Pout, married film director Roger Vadim?	*Brigitte Bardot*
8 What did the first S stand for in the USSR?	*Soviet*
9 Who won a Best Supporting Actor Oscar for his role in the film *City Slickers*?	*Jack Palance*
10 In which ocean are the Solomon Islands?	*Pacific Ocean*

Quiz 53
Question 1

Quiz 53
Question 6

Quiz 55
NATURAL WORLD

Questions	Answers
1 How did the cat-fish get its name?	*It has 'whiskers' round its mouth*
2 A broad-breasted bronze is a breed of which farm bird?	*Turkey*
3 How do mother crocodiles transport their young?	*In their mouths*
4 Which water mammal sometimes saves drowning humans?	*The dolphin*
5 What do mustard seeds and chilli peppers have in common?	*Both are hot to taste*
6 How does the rat snake kill its prey?	*By squeezing (constriction)*
7 Which water mammal gnaws trees and has a large, flat tail?	*Beaver*
8 Which yellow-and-black insect lives in hives and pollinates flowers?	*Bee*
9 Which is the smallest dog – Jack Russell, Chihuahua or Yorkshire terrier?	*Chihuahua*
10 What type of mammal is a Mexican black howler?	*Monkey*

Quiz 56
Question 1

Quiz 56
NATURAL WORLD

Questions	Answers
1 What is a coelacanth – a fish or bird?	*Fish*
2 Which swims as fast as a man runs, the leatherback turtle or bullfrog?	*Leatherback turtle*
3 Almond, hazel, cherry – which is the odd one out?	*Cherry – the others are nuts*
4 Can the octopus change colour?	*Yes*
5 What do you call a male goat?	*Billy goat*
6 Do rabbits eat or avoid stinging nettles?	*They avoid them*
7 Which bird breeds in the Arctic then travels to the Antarctic?	*Arctic tern*
8 What eight-letter word describes any animal that chews the cud?	*Ruminant*
9 Who was the author of the bestselling novel *The Da Vinci Code*?	*Dan Brown*
10 Do flamingoes gather in shallow lakes or deep sea inlets?	*Shallow lakes*

Quiz 55
Question 6

Quiz 55
Question 8

Quiz 57
GENERAL KNOWLEDGE

Questions	Answers
1 In the US, the state of Virginia was named after which monarch?	*Elizabeth I, the Virgin Queen*
2 In which classic film did Minnesota Fats meet Fast Eddie Felson?	The Hustler
3 Which ceiling took Michelangelo four years to paint?	*The Sistine Chapel ceiling*
4 In which ocean are the Falkland Islands?	*Atlantic Ocean*
5 Which former Mayor of New York received a knighthood from the Queen in February 2002?	*Rudolph Giuliani*
6 "My Darling Clementine" was often sung by which animated hound?	*Huckleberry Hound*
7 Which Japanese city hosted the 1964 Summer Olympics?	*Tokyo*
8 What is the capital of New York state?	*Albany*
9 On which island did the Mafia originate?	*Sicily*
10 In the human body, what are formed by a process called ossification?	*Bones*

Quiz 58
Question 1

Quiz 58

GENERAL KNOWLEDGE

Questions	Answers
1 What sport is played by the Philadelphia Flyers?	*Ice hockey*
2 Who played the title role in the 2002 film comedy *Maid In Manhattan*?	*Jennifer Lopez*
3 Bruno Hauptmann was executed for the kidnap and murder of which famous aviator's son?	*Charles Lindbergh*
4 In the foot, what is the more common name for the hallux?	*The big toe*
5 Which famous artist painted *At the Moulin Rouge*?	*Toulouse-Lautrec*
6 Which US rock star was backed by the Silver Bullet Band?	*Bob Seger*
7 In which country is the headquarters of the Benneton fashion empire?	*Italy*
8 Which cartoon duck, voiced by Clarence Nash, had his debut in *The Little Wise Hen*?	*Donald Duck*
9 Who wrote *Treasure Island*?	*Robert Louis Stevenson*
10 Despite suffering an earthquake in 1985, which city hosted the 1986 Football World Cup?	*Mexico City*

Quiz 57
Question 3

Quiz 57
Question 1

Quiz 59
HISTORY

Questions	Answers
1 What is the name of the boy thieves' ringleader in *Oliver Twist*?	*Fagin*
2 What were the initials of Lawrence of Arabia?	*T.E.*
3 What kind of weapon was a ballista?	*Giant crossbow*
4 Who invented the phonograph, an early kind of record player?	*Thomas Edison*
5 General Franco was dictator of which country?	*Spain*
6 Which planet in our Solar System was discovered in 1930?	*Pluto*
7 What are teachers called in the Jewish religion?	*Rabbis*
8 Which famous structure was built by an Indian emperor as a tomb for his wife?	*The Taj Mahal*
9 Which two teams played in the first cricket Test Match?	*England and Australia*
10 Which military general acquired his nickname after his defence at the Battle of Bull Run?	*Stonewall Jackson*

Quiz 60
Question 4

Quiz 60
Question 2

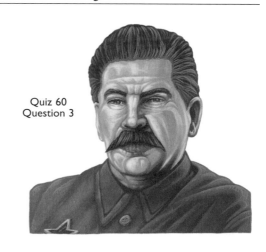

Quiz 60
Question 3

Quiz **60**
HISTORY

Questions	Answers
1 Who painted the famous picture *Water-Lilies* in about 1921?	*Claude Monet*
2 Who did Jacqueline Bouvier marry in 1953?	*John F Kennedy*
3 Which Soviet leader called himself 'Man of Steel'?	*Josef Stalin*
4 What is the symbol of Canada?	*Maple leaf*
5 Who designed a helicopter, a parachute and an armoured car over 500 years ago?	*Leonardo da Vinci*
6 Which Australian folk hero was hanged in Melbourne in 1880?	*Ned Kelly*
7 In which city is the Empire State Building?	*New York*
8 Which war was ended by the Treaty of Appomattox?	*American Civil War*
9 What birds live at the Tower of London?	*Ravens*
10 Who became British prime minister in 1940?	*Winston Churchill*

Quiz 59
Question 4

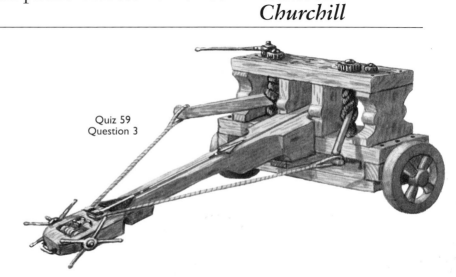

Quiz 59
Question 3

Quiz 61

GENERAL KNOWLEDGE

Questions	Answers
1 Which vegetable would you be eating if ordering *aloo* in an Indian restaurant?	*Potatoes*
2 Florida and New Mexico both share what nickname?	*The Sunshine State*
3 Which car manufacturer made the DB Series?	*Aston Martin*
4 To which country does the island of Rhodes belong?	*Greece*
5 Who played Dr Alan Grant in the film *Jurassic Park*?	*Sam Neill*
6 What article of footwear was named after the military leader who won at Waterloo?	*Wellington boots*
7 What does the DK stand for on the fashion label DKNY?	*Donna Karan*
8 What is herpetology the study of?	*Reptiles*
9 Which TV series starred Fred Savage as a pupil at the Robert F Kennedy High School?	**The Wonder Years**
10 Which word is the collective name for a group of kittens?	*Kindle*

Quiz 62
Question 8

Quiz 62
Question 9

Quiz 62
GENERAL KNOWLEDGE

Questions	Answers
1 Which legal TV drama featured the characters of Arnie Becker and Grace Van Owen?	L.A. Law
2 Which city stages the Formula One Grand Prix in Brazil?	*Rio de Janeiro*
3 Alphabetically, what is Africa's first country?	*Algeria*
4 Who said of Remington shavers, "I liked the shaver so much I bought the company"?	*Victor Kiam*
5 Which religious group is also known as The Society Of Friends?	*The Quakers*
6 The island of Madeira belongs to which country?	*Portugal*
7 In which building in Washington DC does the US Congress meet?	*The Capitol*
8 What does a conchologist collect?	*Seashells*
9 Which car manufacturer makes a model called the Testarossa?	*Ferrari*
10 Who was born in 1847 and went on to found his own company called The Invention Factory?	*Thomas Alva Edison*

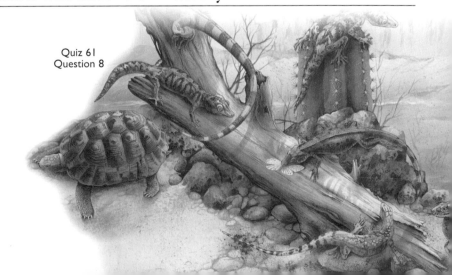

Quiz 61
Question 6

Quiz 61
Question 8

Quiz 61
Question 1

Quiz 63
NATURAL WORLD

Questions	Answers
1 What flying insect can spread the disease malaria?	*Mosquito*
2 Do scorpions produce live young or lay eggs?	*Live young*
3 What B word is the name given to the study of plants?	*Botany*
4 What is the more common name for a eucalyptus tree?	*Gum tree*
5 What name is given to a female foal?	*Filly*
6 A Wessex Saddleback is a breed of which farm animal?	*Pig*
7 What breed of dog is most commonly used by Inuits to pull their sledges?	*Husky*
8 What species of snake has varieties called, green tree, reticulated, Indian and Burmese?	*Python*
9 What dog breed connects Beethoven and the patron saint of mountaineers?	*St Bernard*
10 A rookery is the name given to a collection of which fast-swimming birds?	*Penguins*

Quiz 64
Question 6

Quiz 64
Question 1

Quiz 64
SCIENCE AND MATHS

Questions	Answers
1 What did Thomas Alva Edison invent in 1879 after carrying out 1200 experiments?	*The light bulb*
2 If a century is divided by a score what is the answer?	*Five (100 ÷ 20)*
3 What gas freezes to form dry ice?	*Carbon dioxide*
4 What is one half of a gross?	*72 (144 ÷ 2)*
5 How many weeks are there in a century?	*5200*
6 Enrico Forlanini built the first one in 1905. What was it?	*Hydrofoil*
7 Is the letter I the chemical symbol for iodine, iron or iridium?	*Iodine*
8 If you subtracted a decade from a millennium, how many years would be left?	*990 (1000 – 10)*
9 Which planet would you associate with the chemical symbol of Hg?	*Mercury*
10 How many degrees does a clock's hour hand pass through between 1 am and 6 am?	*150 degrees*

Quiz 63
Question 8

Quiz 63
Question 10

Quiz 65

GENERAL KNOWLEDGE

Questions	Answers
1 Camembert, Emmental and Yarg are types of which food?	*Cheese*
2 Robben Island lies off the coast of which South African city?	*Cape Town*
3 Who played Smee when Dustin Hoffman played Captain Hook?	*Bob Hoskins*
4 Which singer had a posthumous hit record with "Sittin' On The Dock Of The Bay"?	*Otis Redding*
5 What is measured in quires and reams?	*Paper*
6 On 18 May, 1980 which volcano erupted in the US?	*Mount St Helens*
7 What did the city of Leningrad change its name to in 1981?	*St Petersburg*
8 What type of fruit was named after Enoch Bartlett?	*Pear*
9 In the USA, which civil rights leader is commemorated every January?	*Martin Luther King*
10 In 2004, who in the USA held the post of Commander in Chief of the Armed Forces?	*George Bush Jnr*

Quiz 66
Question 8

Quiz 66
Question 10

Quiz 66
GENERAL KNOWLEDGE

Questions	Answers
1 What is the Al short for in the name of the movie star Al Pacino?	*Alfredo*
2 What is the lower age limit for presidents of the USA?	*35*
3 Robert Moog became a pioneer of which electronic musical instrument in the 1960s?	*Synthesizer*
4 Who wrote the play *The Odd Couple*?	*Neil Simon*
5 What is the capital of the Australian state of Queensland?	*Brisbane*
6 Which character was played by Scott Baio in the TV sitcom *Happy Days*?	*Chachi*
7 In which African capital city does the White Nile meet the Blue Nile?	*Khartoum*
8 Sangiovese and Barbera are both varieties of which fruit?	*Grapes*
9 Which singer was born Enrique José Martin Morales?	*Ricky Martin*
10 Which leader of the Mongols was played by John Wayne in the 1955 film *The Conqueror*?	*Genghis Khan*

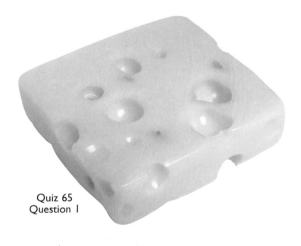

Quiz 65
Question 1

Quiz 65
Question 8

Quiz 67
FOOD AND DRINK

Questions	Answers
1 What did Mark Twain describe as "a cabbage with a college education"?	*Cauliflower*
2 What is the name of the Greek dish made of minced lamb and aubergines?	*Moussaka*
3 By law, which ingredient must French ice cream contain?	*Eggs*
4 In which country did chutney originate?	*India*
5 From what cereal are cornflakes made?	*Maize*
6 What type of fruit is a greengage?	*Plum*
7 Which spice is obtained from the stigmas of the crocus flower?	*Saffron*
8 Blue mountain, mocha and mysore are all varieties of what?	*Coffee*
9 Which dessert has a name that is French for "white food"?	*Blancmange*
10 In which country is the village of Hockheim, from where Hock wine originated?	*Germany*

Quiz 68
Question 3

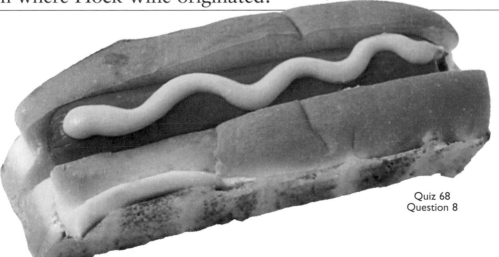

Quiz 68
Question 8

Quiz 68
FOOD AND DRINK

Questions	Answers
1 What is the name of the red pepper that is a chief ingredient of goulash?	*Paprika*
2 From which country did the word 'biscuit' originate?	*France – it means baked twice*
3 What is the name of the fruit that is a cross between a peach and a plum?	*Nectarine*
4 What name is given to a field in which rice is grown?	*Paddy field*
5 Which spice is found in the liqueur kümmel?	*Caraway seeds*
6 What is the only vitamin that is not present in eggs?	*Vitamin C*
7 What is the main ingredient of borscht?	*Beetroot*
8 What is the common name for a hot sausage sandwiched in a roll?	*Hot dog*
9 Which dish of beef in a sour cream was named after a Russian count?	*Beef Stroganoff*
10 What was the name of the monk who is credited with inventing champagne?	*Dom Perignon*

Quiz 67
Question 6

Quiz 67
Question 1

Quiz 69
GENERAL KNOWLEDGE

Questions	Answers
1 How many time zones are there in China?	*One*
2 Is a gaskin part of the front leg or part of the hind leg of a horse?	*Part of the hind leg of a horse*
3 Wandering, marsh and dwarf are all species of which mollusc?	*Snail*
4 Which American football team is known as the Broncos?	*Denver Broncos*
5 Which book opens, 'Alice was beginning to get very tired of sitting by her sister on the bank'?	**Alice's Adventures in Wonderland**
6 Who played the president of the US in *Mars Attacks*?	*Jack Nicholson*
7 What is the national flower of Mexico?	*Dahlia*
8 What is the most populated city in Alaska?	*Anchorage*
9 What surname connects the literary sisters Anne, Emily and Charlotte?	*Brontë*
10 Geronimo was a chief of which Native American tribe?	*Apache*

Quiz 70
Question 4

Quiz 70
Question 8

Quiz 70
GENERAL KNOWLEDGE

Questions

Quiz 69
Question 3

1 What is celebrated on the third Sunday in June in the US?

2 Who created the characters of Brer Fox and Brer Rabbit?

3 Which singer was the world's bestselling female recording artist of the 1990s?

4 A singapura is a miniature breed of which common household pet?

5 In which US city was Legionnaire's Disease first identified?

6 The Four Noble Truths are central to which religion?

7 Sally Bowles is the lead character in which Oscar-winning film musical?

8 Which is the lightest planet in our Solar System?

9 What is the name of the city in Nevada famed for its quick divorces?

10 What South American instrument comprises a gourd full of seeds on a stick?

Answers

Father's Day

Joel Chandler Harris

Mariah Carey

Cat

Philadelphia

Buddhism

Cabaret

Saturn

Reno

Maracas

Quiz 69
Question 7

Quiz 69
Question 10

Quiz 71
THE BIBLE

Questions	Answers
1 Did the three Wise Men travel to see the baby Jesus from the north, south, east or west?	*East*
2 Which creature represented the devil in the Garden of Eden?	*Serpent or snake*
3 Which festival is also known as The Purification of The Virgin Mary?	*Candlemas*
4 What is the sixth Commandment?	*Thou shalt not kill*
5 In the Bible, Jesus was placed in a manger. What is a manger?	*A feeding trough for animals*
6 How many books are there in the Old Testament, 29 or 39?	*39*
7 What does the word advent actually mean?	*Arrival, or coming*
8 In which city is the Wailing Wall?	*Jerusalem*
9 In religious ceremonies, what is burned in a censer?	*Incense*
10 Who did David kill with a stone from his catapult?	*Goliath*

Quiz 72
Question 3

Quiz 72
Question 7

Quiz 72

THE BIBLE

Questions	Answers
1 Who was the first person to see Jesus after his resurrection?	*Mary Magdalene*
2 Who was created from the rib of Adam?	*Eve*
3 An angel appeared to Joseph telling him to take Mary and Jesus to which country?	*Egypt*
4 What is the eighth commandment?	*Thou shalt not steal*
5 What was the name of the stepdaughter of Herod?	*Salome*
6 How many books are there in the New Testament, 27 or 37?	27
7 Who visited Mary to inform her that she was pregnant with the Son of God?	*The Angel Gabriel*
8 Which gospel writer was known as The Beloved Physician?	*Luke*
9 The three Wise Men are believed to be buried in which German cathedral?	*Cologne Cathedral*
10 Who is the patron saint of tax collectors?	*St Matthew*

Quiz 71
Question 2

Quiz 71
Question 8

Quiz 71
Question 10

Quiz 73
GENERAL KNOWLEDGE

Questions	Answers
1 Which word invented by Lewis Carroll is a combination of the words chuckle and snort?	*Chortle*
2 Which US city suffered major earthquakes in 1906 and 1989?	*San Francisco*
3 Calamine is obtained from which chemical element?	*Zinc*
4 What, in ancient Greece, was an amphora?	*A two-handled storage jar*
5 Which race, over 200 laps, is started with the words 'Gentlemen, start your engines'?	*Indianapolis 500*
6 What was the last name of Bonnie of Bonnie and Clyde fame?	*Parker*
7 Would you find a crab spider hiding on a flower or in the sand on a beach?	*Hiding on flower*
8 Brian Lara is a famous player of which sport?	*Cricket*
9 In which film did Barbara Streisand sing "Second Hand Rose"?	Funny Girl
10 Which actress was born Sophia Scicolini?	*Sophia Loren*

Quiz 74
Question 8

Quiz 74
Question 4

Quiz 74
GENERAL KNOWLEDGE

Questions	Answers
1 In the Peanuts cartoon strip, what is the name of the feathered companion of Snoopy?	*Woodstock*
2 What K was the nickname given to the original Dutch settlers of New York?	*Knickerbockers*
3 Who wrote the novel *Born Free*?	*Joy Adamson*
4 In November 2000, who became Senator of New York State?	*Hillary Clinton*
5 In *The Lord Of The Rings* who is the maker of the ring?	*Sauron*
6 The name of which Canadian city means Mount Royal?	*Montreal*
7 In which country did the medical procedure of acupuncture originate?	*China*
8 What is the occupation of Krusty in *The Simpsons* cartoon series?	*Clown*
9 How many successive Wimbledon titles did Bjorn Borg win?	*Five*
10 Which sporting legend did the New York Yankees buy from the Boston Red Sox in 1921?	*Babe Ruth*

Quiz 73
Question 8

Quiz 73
Question 7

Quiz 75
NATURAL WORLD

Questions	Answers
1 Which has the beautiful tail, the female peahen or the male peacock?	*Male peacock*
2 What is the largest fish?	*Whale shark*
3 What breed of dog was named after an Adriatic coast of Yugoslavia?	*Dalmatian*
4 Are any bats vegetarian?	*Yes – fruit bats*
5 What is the alternative 'canine' name for the rock salmon?	*Dogfish*
6 What is the female equivalent of a colt?	*Filly*
7 Does sunshine make lizards sleep or become active?	*It makes them become active*
8 What is the heaviest land mammal after an elephant?	*Hippopotamus*
9 Which member of the horse family has stripes?	*Zebra*
10 How many legs do arachnids have?	*Eight*

Quiz 76
Question 9

Quiz 76
NATURAL WORLD

Questions	Answers
1 What animal lives in the leaves of the eucalyptus tree?	*Koala*
2 What animal does the adjective leonine refer to?	*Lion*
3 What name is given to a female hedgehog?	*Sow*
4 A labour is the collective noun for which burrowing animal?	*Mole*
5 Do coconuts float?	*Yes*
6 What does a sardine become on reaching adulthood?	*Pilchard*
7 Which eats the most each year, a large snake or a small rat?	*A small rat*
8 By what three-letter name is the wildebeest also known?	*Gnu*
9 Which land mammal has the highest blood pressure?	*Giraffe*
10 What is a shark's skeleton made of?	*Cartilage*

Quiz 75
Question 1

Quiz 77

GENERAL KNOWLEDGE

Questions	Answers
1 What is ebony?	A hard, black wood
2 What type of vehicle is an *Electra Glide*?	*Motorcycle*
3 Were there any people around when the dinosaurs lived?	*No*
4 Which major armed conflict began on 12th April 1861?	*The US Civil War*
5 Which country hosts the only Grand Slam tennis tournament in the Southern Hemisphere?	*Australia*
6 What famous building was completed in 1889 for the Paris Exhibition?	*The Eiffel Tower*
7 After whom was Hudson Bay named?	*Henry Hudson*
8 Which Disney film featured the song "Never Smile at a Crocodile"?	Peter Pan
9 A famous motor rally that begins in Paris ends in which city in Senegal?	*Dakar*
10 In which city is the novel and film *Quo Vadis* set?	*Rome*

Quiz 78
Question 8

Quiz 78
Question 3

Quiz 78
GENERAL KNOWLEDGE

Questions	Answers
1 In the body, which is bigger, an artery or a vein?	*A vein*
2 The name of which month is derived from the Latin for ten?	*December*
3 In the Winnie-the-Pooh stories, what sort of creature is Roo?	*Baby kangaroo*
4 Addis Ababa is the capital of which African country?	*Ethiopia*
5 What is the first name of Scully in *The X Files*?	*Dana*
6 What is the singular of opera?	*Opus*
7 On which US river does the Grand Coulee Dam stand?	*Columbia River*
8 Native to central Africa, what is the largest anthropoid ape?	*Gorilla*
9 Which motorcycle manufacturer makes a model called the *Gold Wing*?	*Honda*
10 Which is the only metal that is liquid at room temperature?	**Mercury**

Quiz 77
Question 5

Quiz 77
Question 2

Questions	Answers
1 In which film did Jim Carrey play Lloyd Christmas?	**Dumb and Dumber**
2 Which 2005 romantic comedy co-starred Jane Fonda and Jennifer Lopez?	**Monster-In-Law**
3 In a Christmas special, what did Mr Bean buy his teddy bear as a Christmas present?	*A pair of eyes*
4 Who played the British wife of Ross in *Friends*?	*Helen Baxendale*
5 In which Bond film did Halle Berry play the role of Jinx?	**Die Another Day**
6 The film *Shakespeare In Love* told the story behind the making of which play?	**Romeo And Juliet**
7 In which 2005 film did Tom Hanks travel on a train bound for the North Pole?	**The Polar Express**
8 Which actor, better known for his Bond roles, played Professor Henry Jones in a 1989 film?	*Sean Connery*
9 In which 2004 film did Dennis Quaid play a climatologist called Jack Hall?	**The Day After Tomorrow**
10 Which actress played Dr Ellie Satler in *Jurassic Park*?	*Laura Dern*

Quiz 80
Question 5

Quiz 80
Question 4

Questions	Answers
1 Which composer did Kevin Kline portray in the 2004 film *De-Lovely*?	*Cole Porter*
2 In which TV show does a teenage witch live with her aunts and a talking cat?	**Sabrina the Teenage Witch**
3 In the film *Great Balls of Fire!*, which rock and roller was played by Dennis Quaid?	*Jerry Lee Lewis*
4 Who won a Best Supporting Actress Oscar for her role in the film *Ghost*?	**Whoopi Goldberg**
5 What was Mr Bean looking for when he got his head stuck in a giant turkey?	*His watch*
6 Who won a Best Director Oscar for the film *Titanic*?	*James Cameron*
7 Which classic Christmas film starring James Stewart features an angel called Clarence?	**It's A Wonderful Life**
8 Who played the Bond girl, Pussy Galore and the Avenger, Cathy Gale?	*Honor Blackman*
9 Who played the role of Clark Griswold in the film *National Lampoon's Christmas Vacation*?	*Chevy Chase*
10 In which film did Anthony Hopkins say, "I'm having an old friend for dinner"?	**Silence of the Lambs**

Quiz 79
Question 7

Quiz 81
GENERAL KNOWLEDGE

Questions	Answers
1 Which US state is known as The Grand Canyon state?	*Arizona*
2 Which editor of the *Los Angeles Tribune* was played on TV by Ed Asner?	*Lou Grant*
3 Alto, bass, contrabass and tenor are all sizes of which brass instrument?	*Trombone*
4 Name the former dictator of Cambodia who died in 1998.	*Pol Pot*
5 Who plays Tony Soprano in the Mafia drama *The Sopranos*?	*James Gandolfini*
6 On which New York island is Wall Street?	*Manhattan*
7 Which musical featured the song "Hopelessly Devoted To You"?	Grease
8 Which flying mammals use echo-location to find food?	*Bats*
9 Which bank robber, shot dead by FBI agents in 1934, was America's first Public Enemy No 1?	*John Dillinger*
10 In which 1960s sitcom did Barbara Eden play a female genie called Jeanie?	I Dream of Jeanie

Quiz 82
Question 7

Quiz 82
Question 8

Quiz 82
GENERAL KNOWLEDGE

Questions	Answers
1 Which transatlantic 1960s hit opened with the line 'There is a house in New Orleans'?	*"House Of The Rising Sun"*
2 On which river is the Hoover Dam?	*Colorado River*
3 Which famous boxer was born Rocco Marchegiano?	*Rocky Marciano*
4 Who penned the autobiography *Rhinestone Cowboy*?	*Glen Campbell*
5 Who wrote the novels *The Firm* and *The Pelican Brief*?	*John Grisham*
6 What does the I stand for in CIA and MI5?	*Intelligence*
7 What name is given to a young beaver?	*Kitten*
8 In which capital city is Oscar Wilde buried?	*Paris*
9 What is the last name of Dorothy in *The Wizard Of Oz*?	*Gale*
10 Which US state is known as The Last Frontier?	*Alaska*

Quiz 81
Question 8

Quiz 81
Question 3

Quiz 83
HISTORY

Questions	Answers
1 Who was known as 'the Lady with the Lamp'?	*Florence Nightingale*
2 Who founded the Philadelphia police force in 1737?	*Benjamin Franklin*
3 What part of armour is a greave?	*Protection for the shin*
4 The Pont Neuf is the oldest what in Paris?	*Bridge*
5 In which city is Michelangelo's statue of *David*?	*Florence*
6 Which country did Confucius come from?	*China*
7 How many symphonies did Beethoven write?	*Nine*
8 In which city is St Paul's Cathedral?	*London*
9 What was a Chinese junk?	*Sailing ship*
10 Which scientist gave his name to the unit of capacitance, the Farad?	*Michael Faraday*

Quiz 84
Question 10

Quiz 84
Question 9

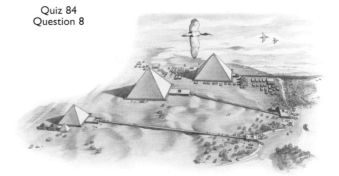

Quiz 84
Question 8

Quiz 84
HISTORY

Questions	Answers
1 In which year was the silicon chip invented: 1925, 1955 or 1975?	*1975*
2 Which US president was forced to resign in 1974?	*Richard Nixon*
3 What was the nickname of pirate Edward Teach?	*Blackbeard*
4 Who wrote the novel *Jane Eyre*?	*Charlotte Brontë*
5 The sinking of which vessel was instrumental in the USA entering World War I?	Lusitania
6 Which was the first organization to win the Nobel Peace Prize twice?	*International Red Cross*
7 What kind of engine was Thomas Newcomen famous for inventing?	*Steam engine*
8 Which Wonder of the World was built on the orders of Egyptian king Cheops?	*The Great Pyramid*
9 How many sets of wings had a triplane?	*Three*
10 Which Chinese leader wrote down his thoughts in *The Little Red Book*?	*Chairman Mao*

Quiz 83
Question 3

Quiz 83
Question 10

Quiz 85

GENERAL KNOWLEDGE

Questions	Answers
1 Which marine creature has eyes on stalks, is blue before cooked, and red when cooked?	*Lobster*
2 The Beaufort Sea is part of which ocean?	*Arctic Ocean*
3 What is the canine equivalent of a fingerprint for identification purposes?	*Nose print*
4 In Australia, in which month of the year does the longest day fall?	*December*
5 Which inert gas is used to illuminate street signs?	*Neon*
6 What is the world's largest bird after the ostrich?	*Emu*
7 Which European country's international car registration plate is denoted by the letter S?	*Sweden*
8 What is the most common surname in Great Britain?	*Smith*
9 What type of musical note is equal in length to two quavers?	*Crotchet*
10 Which is the smallest prime number?	*1*

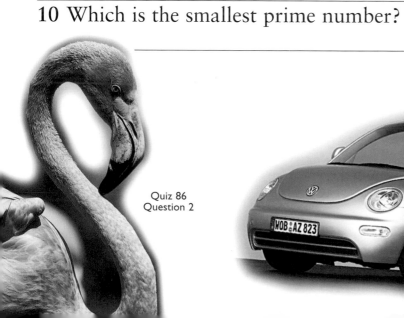

Quiz 86
Question 2

Quiz 86
Question 5

Quiz 86

GENERAL KNOWLEDGE

Questions	Answers
1 Who is the father of the actor Emilio Estevez?	*Martin Sheen*
2 Which very tall and long-legged wading bird is usually pink?	*The flamingo*
3 Who played Qui-Gon Jinn in the film *Star Wars: Episode 1 – The Phantom Menace*?	*Liam Neeson*
4 What is the name of the editor of *The Daily Planet*?	*Perry White*
5 What kind of car is Herbie in the Disney films?	*Volkswagen beetle*
6 Which US city is nicknamed The Cowboy City of the World?	*Dodge City*
7 Who discovered penicillin	**Alexander Fleming**
8 What is the capital of Finland?	*Helsinki*
9 Which famous silent film star had the middle name of Spencer?	*Charlie Chaplin*
10 What does the R stand for in the US record label RCA?	*Radio*

Quiz 85
Question 9

Quiz 85
Question 3

Quiz 85
Question 1

Quiz 87

FOOD AND DRINK

Questions	Answers
1 Which sauce traditionally accompanies turkey?	*Cranberry sauce*
2 What name is given to a dish of toast cooked with ham, eggs and hollandaise sauce?	*Eggs Benedict*
3 Which ingredient gives English mustard its heat?	*Mustard seeds*
4 Are female or male hop plants used when making beer?	*Female*
5 Amontillado, Oloroso and Cream are all varieties of which drink?	*Sherry*
6 What sweet substance is used in the diet of diabetics and weight watchers?	*Saccharin*
7 Which five-letter word is the name for a young turkey?	*Poult*
8 Which small fruit is named after a flightless New Zealand bird?	*Kiwi*
9 Which type of sweet would you associate with a phrase often uttered by Scrooge?	*Humbug*
10 Retsina is the national wine of which country?	*Greece*

Quiz 88
Question 8

Quiz 88
Question 6

Quiz 88
FOOD AND DRINK

Questions	Answers
1 Brazil nuts originated in which South American country?	*Bolivia*
2 In Shakespeare's *Hamlet*, which herb is said to be for remembrance?	*Rosemary*
3 On which continent were turkeys first found?	*North America*
4 In which US state did the drink of Jack Daniels originate?	*Tennessee*
5 Which three words sung by Band Aid preceded "Let them know it's Christmas time"?	*Feed the world*
6 What are the following: Rome Beauty, Jonathan, Cortland and Winesap?	*Types of apple*
7 What boy's name is also the name for a male turkey?	*Tom*
8 Korma, vindaloo and tikka are all which type of food?	*Curry*
9 What is the common name for an advocaat and lemonade cocktail?	*Snowball*
10 Is a cucumber a fruit or a vegetable?	*Fruit*

Quiz 87
Question 8

Quiz 87
Question 10

Quiz 89
GENERAL KNOWLEDGE

Questions	Answers
1 During World War II, what nickname was given to the RAF 617 Squadron?	*The Dam Busters*
2 *Citizen Jane* was the autobiography of which actress?	*Jane Fonda*
3 Which Polish electrician won the Nobel Peace Prize in 1983?	*Lech Walesa*
4 Who is the bestselling author of the *His Dark Materials* trilogy?	*Philip Pullman*
5 Who played Jane in six films when Johnny Weismuller played Tarzan?	*Maureen O'Sullivan*
6 Which bird drums and yaffles?	*Woodpecker*
7 In which country was the 2001 version of *The Lord of the Rings* filmed?	*New Zealand*
8 What word can be a make of car, a type of flower and a position in yoga?	*Lotus*
9 In the Bible, what are numbered in the Book of Numbers?	*The tribes of Israel*
10 Which actress ex-wife of Tony Curtis was born Jeanette Morrison?	*Janet Leigh*

Quiz 90
Question 9

Quiz 90
Question 7

Quiz 90
GENERAL KNOWLEDGE

Questions	Answers
1 What is the nationality of Pope Benedict XVI?	*German*
2 Which saint is associated with the French town of Lourdes?	*Bernadette*
3 How is Lake Tiberias better known in the Bible?	*Sea of Galilee*
4 Which actress was the first wife of Ronald Reagan?	*Jane Wyman*
5 *To Hell And Back* is the autobiography of which highly decorated American war hero?	*Audie Murphy*
6 Which one-time film partner of Dean Martin was born Joseph Levitch?	*Jerry Lewis*
7 The oil of which spice is used as a traditional cure for toothache?	*Cloves*
8 On a map, a line called an isotherm connects areas of equal what?	*Temperature*
9 What type of animal is Flower in the Disney film *Bambi*?	*Skunk*
10 Which blood group can receive blood from any other blood group?	*AB*

Quiz 89
Question 7

Quiz 89
Question 6

Quiz 91
THE BIBLE

Questions	Answers
1 What bird is said to have plucked a thorn from Jesus at his crucifixion?	*Robin*
2 In the Bible, what swallowed Jonah?	*Whale (big fish)*
3 How are Balthazar, Melchior and Gaspar collectively known?	*The Three Wise Men*
4 Which book of the Bible starts with the words 'In the beginning'?	*Genesis*
5 Which bird did Noah send out first from the ark?	*Raven*
6 In what kind of building was Jesus born?	*Stable*
7 What was the first book of the New Testament to mention the birth of Jesus?	*St Matthew*
8 What is the third book of the Bible?	*Leviticus*
9 In which village was Jesus born?	*Bethlehem*
10 What is myrrh?	*Gum resin*

Quiz 92
Question 7

Quiz 92
Question 9

Quiz 92
THE BIBLE

Questions	Answers
1 What gift did Balthazar bring?	*Frankincense*
2 According to the Bible, what did God create on the first day?	*Heaven and Earth*
3 What was the name of the Roman Procurator who ordered the crucifixion of Jesus?	*Pontius Pilate*
4 In which language was the New Testament originally written?	*Greek*
5 Who replaced Judas Iscariot as one of the 12 apostles?	*Matthias*
6 What is the second book of the Bible?	*Exodus*
7 What food did John the Baptist eat when he lived in the desert?	*Locusts and wild honey*
8 How many people attended the Last Supper?	*13*
9 From where did the disciples see Jesus walk on water?	*A boat*
10 Who died first, Cain or Abel?	*Abel*

Quiz 91
Question 2

Quiz 91
Question 6

Quiz 93
GENERAL KNOWLEDGE

Questions	Answers
1 The country of Croatia forms a coastline on which sea?	*Adriatic Sea*
2 The sap of which tree is called latex?	*The rubber tree*
3 Tinnitus affects which organ of the body?	*The ear*
4 Which is the largest state in Australia?	*Western Australia*
5 What is the name of the protein that forms hair and nails?	*Keratin*
6 What kind of creature is a sand mason – a crab or a worm?	*Worm*
7 What is the name given to objects thrown overboard on a ship?	*Jetsam*
8 Who played Inspector Steve Keller in the TV drama *The Streets of San Francisco*?	*Michael Douglas*
9 By what three initials is deoxyribonucleic acid better known?	*DNA*
10 Kathy Kane is the secret identity of which super heroine?	*Batwoman*

Quiz 94
Question 6

Quiz 94
Question 8

Quiz 94
GENERAL KNOWLEDGE

Questions	Answers
1 Which dinosaur has a name that means 'thunder lizard'?	**Brontosaurus**
2 Which park is known as the Lungs of New York?	*Central Park*
3 By what three initials is polyvinyl chloride better known?	*PVC*
4 Which novel about a giant white whale was written by Herman Melville?	**Moby Dick**
5 Which US state provided the setting for the TV series *Magnum PI*?	*Hawaii*
6 In which organ of the body is the pituitary gland?	*Brain*
7 Which actress was married to Charles Bronson and David McCallum?	*Jill Ireland*
8 Marsh, gos and sparrow are all types of which bird of prey?	*Hawk*
9 What is the French-sounding name of the state capital of Louisiana?	*Baton Rouge*
10 Which composer wrote the most concertos, Verdi or Vivaldi?	*Vivaldi*

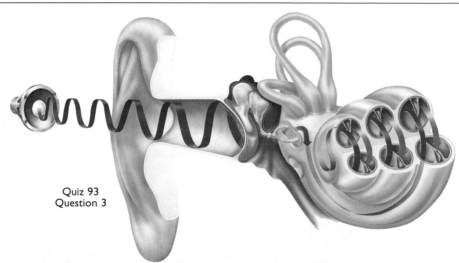

Quiz 93
Question 3

Quiz 95
LANGUAGES

Questions	Answers
1 From which language did the word rabbi originate?	*Hebrew*
2 What is the official language of Cuba?	*Spanish*
3 What does Feng Shui mean in English?	*Wind and water*
4 Which commonly used Latin phrase literally means 'the other way round'?	*Vice versa*
5 What type of pea has a French name that means 'eat all' in English?	*Mange tout*
6 Which country has four official languages – French, German, Italian and Romansch?	*Switzerland*
7 If a meeting is held *in camera*, what does this mean?	*In secret*
8 Which five-letter word is given to a circular coral reef on top of a submerged mountain?	*Atoll*
9 What does the word renaissance mean?	*Rebirth*
10 What branch of mathematics was named after the Latin for pebble?	*Calculus*

Quiz 96
Question 7

Quiz 96
Question 4

Quiz 96
LANGUAGES

Questions	Answers
1 What is the French word for library?	*Bibliotheque*
2 What number does the prefix kilo signify?	*1000*
3 What is the official language of Iraq?	*Arabic*
4 From what language does the word anorak derive?	*Inuit*
5 Which word of Italian origin literally means 'scratched drawings'?	*Sgraffito*
6 What is the official language of Pakistan?	*Urdu*
7 Which is the only vowel that does not appear on the top row of a computer keyboard?	*A*
8 Which gas was named after the Greek word for Sun?	*Helium*
9 Does the word festinate mean hungry, hasty or helpful?	*Hasty*
10 What is the official language of the Fiji Islands?	*English*

Quiz 95
Question 3

Quiz 95
Question 5

Quiz 97
GENERAL KNOWLEDGE

Questions	Answers
1 The exterior of the Taj Mahal is made from which material?	*Marble*
2 Which large farm animal has four stomachs?	*Cow*
3 Who composed "The Maple Leaf Rag"?	*Scott Joplin*
4 Planet Hollywood was opened by Bruce Willis, Sylvester Stallone and who else?	*Arnold Schwarzenegger*
5 In which German city is the underground railway system called the *U-bahn*?	*Berlin*
6 What is the more common name for a pyrotechnic display?	*Fireworks display*
7 In which city was the first Hard Rock Café opened in 1971?	*London*
8 Barcelona is the capital of which region of Spain?	*Catalonia*
9 Which US state boasts the most gambling casinos?	*Nevada*
10 In which country was the lost city of the Incas rediscovered in 1911?	*Peru*

Quiz 98
Question 10

Quiz 98

GENERAL KNOWLEDGE

Questions	Answers
1 Which building in Chicago boasts 110 storeys?	*The Sears Tower*
2 Which actor has played Robin Hood, James Bond, and Richard the Lionheart?	*Sean Connery*
3 What type of beans are used to make baked beans?	*Haricot*
4 Who narrated the Joel Chandler Harris stories about Brer Fox and Brer Rabbit?	*Uncle Remus*
5 What name is given to the chalice used by Jesus at the Last Supper?	*The Holy Grail*
6 Who wrote the original novel of *Les Miserables*?	*Victor Hugo*
7 Which English king led his army to victory at Agincourt?	*Henry V*
8 In which comedy drama series did Cybill Shepherd play Maddie Hayes?	Moonlighting
9 Which giant birds once roamed New Zealand?	*Moas*
10 Found in Rome, what is the name of the largest Christian church in the world?	*St Peter's*

Quiz 97
Question I

Quiz 97
Question 2

Quiz 97
Question 6

Quiz 99

NATURAL WORLD

Questions	Answers
1 Eastern Lowland and Cross River are both species of which animal?	*Gorilla*
2 Which animal has an aboriginal name meaning 'I don't understand'?	*The kangaroo*
3 What name is given to the furry covering on the newly formed antlers of deers?	*Velvet*
4 Are the ears of a cricket on its front legs or its back legs?	*Front legs*
5 Which animal is also known as the prairie wolf?	*Coyote*
6 Which bird lays the smallest eggs?	*Hummingbird*
7 What type of animal is a barracuda?	*A fish*
8 What is a water moccasin?	*Snake*
9 What does a pinniped have instead of feet?	*Flippers*
10 Is a manatee also known as a seahorse, a sea lion or a sea cow?	*Sea cow*

Quiz 100
Question 9

Quiz 100
Question 1

Quiz 100
NATURAL WORLD

Questions	Answers
1 Which creature is the largest reptile?	*The crocodile*
2 How many eyes does a bee have: five, six or seven?	*Five*
3 What is the stage between egg and chrysalis in moths?	*Caterpillar or larva*
4 What is a hartebeest?	*Antelope*
5 What type of bird lives in an eyrie?	*Eagle*
6 Spectacled and Kodiak are both species of which animal?	*Bear*
7 Which bird has nostrils at the tip of its beak?	*Kiwi*
8 Is a Tasmanian devil a rodent or a marsupial?	*Marsupial*
9 What is the world's largest invertebrate creature?	*Giant squid*
10 Which bird is the national symbol of Chile?	*Condor*

Quiz 99
Question 6

Quiz 99
Question 1

Quiz 101
GENERAL KNOWLEDGE

Questions	Answers
1 What is the name of the highest waterfall in the US?	*Yosemite Falls*
2 Which crooner was born Nathaniel Adams?	*Nat King Cole*
3 Known as the black box, is an aircraft's flight recorder black, blue or orange?	*Orange*
4 Which actress played a psychotic fan in the film *Misery*?	*Kathy Bates*
5 Sam, Merry and Pippin are all names of what in the novel *The Lord of the Rings*?	*Hobbits*
6 In which city is Euro Disney?	*Paris*
7 Which US president was a former peanut farmer?	*Jimmy Carter*
8 Chieftain and Sherman are both types of what?	*Tank*
9 On what shape of pitch is an Australian Rules football match played?	*Oval*
10 Which famous car manufacturer was born in the US in 1863 and died in 1947?	*Henry Ford*

Quiz 102
Question 2

Quiz 102
GENERAL KNOWLEDGE

Questions	Answers
1 What is the term for a person who has assets of over a thousand million dollars?	*A billionaire*
2 What British liner sank on 7 May, 1915?	Lusitania
3 What is the popular name for a Boeing 747? *Quiz 101 Question 3*	*Jumbo jet*
4 In what year did Ronald Reagan and the Pope survive assassination attempts?	*1981*
5 What is the indigenous religion of Japan called?	*Shinto*
6 What name is given to the last man on a tug-of-war team?	*Anchorman*
7 In which US TV series did Sorrel Brooke play Boss Hogg?	The Dukes of Hazzard
8 Which species of bear has white fur and black skin?	*Polar bear*
9 In the first decade of the 20th century, what became the capital of Australia?	*Canberra*
10 What did Thomas Chippendale make?	*Furniture*

Quiz 101
Question 8

Quiz 103
MUSIC

Questions	Answers
1 What is the 'regal' stage name of the singer born Dana Owens?	Queen Latifah
2 True or false, Moby is a direct descendent of Herman Melville the author of *Moby Dick*?	True
3 What were the names of the two little boys in the Rolf Harris Christmas hit song?	Joe and Jack
4 According to the song, what did Molly Malone sell in the streets of Dublin?	Cockles and mussels
5 "Somethin' Stupid" was a Christmas hit in 2001. Who sang it originally?	Frank and Nancy Sinatra
6 Which Cuban singer enjoyed a 1992 festive hit with "Christmas Through Your Eyes"?	Gloria Estefan
7 What kind of Christmas did Elvis Presley have in the 1964 charts?	"Blue Christmas"
8 Which group did Paul McCartney form after the break up of The Beatles?	Wings
9 Which Bond theme did Sheena Easton perform?	"For Your Eyes Only"
10 What was Elvis Presley's middle name?	Aaron

Quiz 104 Question 1

Quiz 104
MUSIC

Questions	Answers
1 How many drummers were drumming in "The 12 Days of Christmas"?	*12*
2 Which musical featured the songs "There Ain't Nothing Like a Dame" and "Happy Talk"?	South Pacific
3 Which school subject is the last word of the song "Rudolph the Red-Nosed Reindeer"?	*History*
4 Tom Jones performed the theme for which Bond film?	Thunderball
5 In which decade was the song "White Christmas" written?	*1940s*
6 Which country and western singer starred in the film *Rocky Mountain Christmas*?	*John Denver*
7 Which American rock star had a 1985 top 10 hit with "Santa Claus Is Coming To Town"?	*Bruce Springsteen*
8 "Cathy's Clown" and "Bye Bye Love" were hits for which recording duo?	*Everly Brothers*
9 The Pips provide the backing vocals for which female singer?	*Gladys Knight*
10 Which dance provided Little Eva with her biggest hit?	*"The Locomotion"*

Quiz 103
Question 5

Quiz 105

GENERAL KNOWLEDGE

Questions	Answers
1 Which capital city of Liberia was named after a US president?	*Monrovia, after James Monroe*
2 What do the initials DVD stand for?	*Digital Versatile Disc*
3 Which bird provided the title of a worldwide instrumental hit for Fleetwood Mac in 1969?	*Albatross*
4 What is the largest state of the US that forms a border with Mexico?	*Texas*
5 Which adventure novel by H. Rider Haggard features the characters of Twala and Umbopa?	**King Solomon's Mines**
6 In Greek mythology, which island was home to the labyrinth where the Minotaur lived?	*Crete*
7 In the 1997 film *Michael*, what did John Travolta play the part of?	*An angel*
8 What type of snakes appeared on the crowns of Egyptian pharaohs?	*Cobras*
9 What are the lower chambers of the heart called?	*Ventricles*
10 Under what name did Marvin Lee Aday sing "Paradise By The Dashboard Light"?	*Meatloaf*

Quiz 106
Question 7

Quiz 106
GENERAL KNOWLEDGE

Questions	Answers
1 What is the oldest university in the US?	*Harvard*
2 What do the initials VDU stand for?	*Visual Display Unit*
3 What species of beetle was considered sacred in ancient Egypt?	*Scarab*
4 Which former Mayor of Cincinnati compered the Miss World pageant in 2000?	*Jerry Springer*
5 In which city was the Constitution of the USA signed?	*Philadelphia*
6 Which film was directed by Stanley Kubrick and featured a computer called Hal 9000?	**2001 A Space Odyssey**
7 Hypnos is the Greek god of what?	*Sleep*
8 What falls on the second Sunday of May in the US and the fourth Sunday of Lent in the UK?	*Mother's Day*
9 How did Louise Brown make medical history in 1978?	*She was the first test tube baby*
10 Which state of the USA has the highest population?	*California*

Quiz 105
Question 3

Quiz 105
Question 7

Quiz 105
Question 8

Quiz 107
HISTORY

Questions	Answers
1 Which Native American people defeated Custer at the Little Big Horn?	*Sioux*
2 Who led the second team that reached the South Pole ?	*R F Scott*
3 What was the last battle fought by Horatio Nelson?	*Trafalgar*
4 Who did Britain fight in the Opium War of 1839?	*The Chinese*
5 Which emperor announced in 1946 that he was no longer a god?	*Hirohito of Japan*
6 Who wrote *The Lord of the Flies*?	*William Golding*
7 At which siege did Davy Crockett die in 1836?	*The Alamo*
8 Who is also known as the 'Godfather of soul'?	*James Brown*
9 Which waterfall in Africa was named after a British queen?	*Victoria Falls*
10 Which pair of aviators first flew the Atlantic in 1919?	*John Alcock and Arthur Brown*

Quiz 108
Question 8

Quiz 108
Question 5

Quiz 108
HISTORY

Questions	Answers
1 What attachment for rifles is also used to quieten car exhausts?	*Silencer*
2 In which country was Emiliano Zapata a freedom fighter?	*Mexico*
3 Of which country was Jan Smuts the prime minister in 1919?	*South Africa*
4 What South African language is derived from Dutch?	*Afrikaans*
5 Which woman starred in Buffalo Bill's Wild West Show?	*Annie Oakley*
6 Which Swiss mountain was first climbed by Edward Whymper in 1865?	*The Matterhorn*
7 In which year was the modern state of Israel founded?	*1948*
8 What instrument did Django Reinhardt play?	*Guitar*
9 Who was Tom Cruise married to from 1987 to 1990?	*Mimi Rogers*
10 Which European country conquered Brazil?	*Portugal*

Quiz 107
Question 5

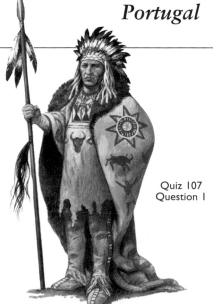

Quiz 107
Question 1

Quiz **109**
GENERAL KNOWLEDGE

Questions	Answers
1 Who painted *The Birth of Venus*?	*Sandro Botticelli*
2 The word Nippon is inscribed on the stamps of which country?	*Japan*
3 After whom is the orbital Space Telescope named?	*Edwin Hubble*
4 What nationality was the writer Hans Christian Andersen?	*Danish*
5 Which is the only big cat with non retractable claws?	*Cheetah*
6 What was the name of the comet that was visible from Earth during 1997?	*Hale-Bopp*
7 Which infamous San Francisco prison was closed in 1963?	*Alcatraz*
8 On a yacht, are the 'sheets' ropes or sails?	*Ropes*
9 What does *Triceratops* mean?	*Three-horned face*
10 Which US baseball team are called the Astros?	*Houston*

Quiz 110
Question 8

Quiz 110
Question 2

Quiz 110
GENERAL KNOWLEDGE

Questions	Answers
1 What nationality was the scientist and chemist Alfred Nobel?	*Swedish*
2 Which part of its body does a thresher shark use to stun its prey?	*Its tail*
3 Who acquired the nickname of 'Stormin' Norman' during the Gulf War?	*Norman Schwarzkopf*
4 What is the largest lake in Africa?	*Lake Victoria*
5 Which actor born in the US in 1928 played Dangerman and The Prisoner on TV?	*Patrick McGoohan*
6 Is Australia's rugby league team nicknamed The Kangaroos or The Wallabies?	*The Kangaroos*
7 What was the nationality of Pope John Paul II?	*Polish*
8 Triton is the largest moon of which planet?	*Neptune*
9 Monarch and Birdwing are both species of which insect?	*Butterfly*
10 Which war was fought between 1950 and 1953?	*The Korean War*

Quiz 109
Question 8

Quiz 109
Question 5

Quiz 111
NATURAL WORLD

Questions	Answers
1 Whooper and trumpeter are both varieties of which bird?	*Swan*
2 What do hummingbirds feed on?	*Nectar from flowers*
3 What is the alternative name for a fish hawk?	*Osprey*
4 What name is given to the young of a grouse?	*Poult*
5 Which bird, native to New Zealand, was declared extinct in the early 19th century?	*Moa*
6 A duck is a palmiped. What does this mean?	*It has webbed feet*
7 What U word is the collective name for a group of ravens?	*An unkindness*
8 Where is the gizzard in a bird's body?	*In the stomach*
9 Which bird, associated with Christmas, is the official state bird of Michigan and Wisconsin?	*Robin*
10 Which bird lays an egg that can have a diameter of up to 15 cm?	*Ostrich*

Quiz 112
Question 9

Quiz 112
Question 5

Quiz 112
NATURAL WORLD

Questions	Answers
1 What name is given to the young of a pigeon?	*Squab*
2 Which is the official state bird of Texas and Tennessee?	*Mockingbird*
3 What is the alternative name for the butcher bird?	*Shrike*
4 What is the most common member of the crow family?	*Rook*
5 Which bird, native to the island of Mauritius, became extinct in the late 17th century?	*Dodo*
6 To which family of birds does the mynah bird belong?	*Starling*
7 Egyptian, Canada and greylag are all species of which bird?	*Goose*
8 What E word is the collective name for a group of larks?	*An exaltation*
9 Which is the smallest species of owl?	*Elf owl*
10 How many toes does an emu have on each foot?	*Three*

Quiz 111
Question 10

Quiz 113

GENERAL KNOWLEDGE

Questions	Answers
1 Who was the Vice President of George Bush Senior?	*Dan Quayle*
2 Which Oriental detective was created by Earl Biggers?	*Charlie Chan*
3 What is the common name for the only parallel that divides the Earth into hemispheres?	*Equator*
4 Iberia is the national airline of which European country?	*Spain*
5 Is the letter L on the top, middle or bottom row of a computer keyboard?	*Middle*
6 Which organs remove waste products from the blood?	*The kidneys*
7 What name is given to a female whale?	*Cow*
8 Which actor became the 40th president of the USA?	*Ronald Reagan*
9 What does a numismatist study?	*Coins*
10 How many sides does a rhombus have?	*Four*

Quiz 114
Question 10

Quiz 114
Question 1

Quiz 114
GENERAL KNOWLEDGE

Questions

1 Which Hollywood icon was born Norma Jean Mortensen in 1926?

2 What is a cummerbund?

Quiz 113
Question 8

3 What name was given to the Chinese peasant uprising of 1900?

4 Which animals are measured in hands, one hand being equivalent to 4 inches?

5 Who was the Vice President of Gerald Ford?

6 Which material is made from the cocoon of a moth?

7 In the Wild West, what did Native Americans call firewater?

8 Which is the largest island in the Mediterranean Sea?

9 How many claws does a dog have?

10 Does vanilla belong to the olive or orchid family?

Answers

Marilyn Monroe

Sash worn around the waist

The Boxer Rebellion

Horses

Nelson Rockefeller

Silk

Whisky

Sicily

18

Orchid

Quiz 113
Question 7

Quiz 115
TV AND FILM

Questions	Answers
1 What is the name of the canine sidekick of The Grinch?	*Max*
2 Who won Oscars for her performances in the films *Norma Rae* and *Places in the Heart*?	*Sally Field*
3 Who played the role of Fox Mulder in *The X Files*?	*David Duchovny*
4 Who played Jonathan Hart in *Hart To Hart*?	*Robert Wagner*
5 Which entertainer was portrayed by Jamie Foxx in the 2004 film *Ray*?	*Ray Charles*
6 In which TV game show do eliminated contestants take the walk of shame?	**The Weakest Link**
7 Which actor arrested a gang of drug dealers at a Christmas tree stand in the film *Lethal Weapon*?	*Mel Gibson*
8 Which song from the film *High Society* lent its name to a worldwide TV quiz show?	***"Who Wants To Be A Millionaire"***
9 In which film did Bing Crosby play the character of Bob Wallace?	**White Christmas**
10 In which decade was the first *Star Wars* film released?	*1970s*

Quiz 116
Question 9

Quiz 116
Question 10

Quiz 116
TV AND FILM

Questions	Answers
1 Who directed the films *Jackie Brown* and *Reservoir Dogs*?	Quentin Tarantino
2 Scott Joplin's "The Entertainer" featured as the theme music for which Oscar-winning film?	**The Sting**
3 In which film, set at Christmas, did Bruce Willis first play the streetwise cop John McClane?	**Die Hard**
4 Which actor was reincarnated as Bobby Ewing in a Southfork shower?	*Patrick Duffy*
5 In which film did Tim Allen play a character who accidentally killed Santa?	**The Santa Clause**
6 What was the title of the first film in which Matt Damon played the spy Jason Bourne?	**The Bourne Identity**
7 Which author does Johnny Depp portray in the film *Finding Neverland*?	*JM Barrie*
8 In which series of films does Christopher Lloyd play Dr Emmett Brown?	**Back to the Future**
9 Who stars as Muhammad Ali in the 2002 film *Ali*?	*Will Smith*
10 Who did Tim Curry play in *Muppet Treasure Island*?	*Long John Silver*

Quiz 115
Question 9

Quiz 115
Question 7

Quiz 117
GENERAL KNOWLEDGE

Questions	Answers
1 In which country was tennis star Martina Navratilova born?	*Czech Republic*
2 Which mammal pollinates bananas?	*Bat*
3 What kind of creatures are Hazel and Bigwig, literary creations of Richard Adams?	*Rabbits*
4 Which Wild West outlaw was born in 1847 and shot dead by Bob Ford in 1882?	*Jesse James*
5 Vladimir Kramnik beat Gary Kasparov to become World Champion at which game?	*Chess*
6 What is the name of the tendon that connects the heel to the calf muscle?	*Achilles tendon*
7 On TV, who left *The Enterprise* to play TJ Hooker?	*William Shatner*
8 In 1999, which pop star was ordained as Mother Bernadette?	*Sinead O'Connor*
9 Was the Leaning Tower of Pisa built in the 11th, 12th or 13th century?	*12th century*
10 Who played the corrupt President Richmond in the 1997 film *Absolute Power*?	*Gene Hackman*

Quiz 118
Question 9

Quiz 118
Question 8

Quiz 118
GENERAL KNOWLEDGE

Questions	Answers
1 In which European country was tennis star John McEnroe born?	*Germany*
2 What was the title of the fourth *Harry Potter* novel released in July 2000?	Harry Potter and The Goblet Of Fire
3 How many points is a bullseye worth in archery?	*Nine*
4 What is the name of Lady Penelope's butler in *Thunderbirds*?	*Parker*
5 Which gas is the most abundant element in the Universe?	*Hydrogen*
6 What fate befell Alice when she drank from a bottle labelled 'Drink Me'?	*She shrank*
7 The novel *Oliver's Story* was a sequel to which bestselling work?	Love Story
8 In the Orwell novel *1984*, the lead character Winston Smith is terrified of which creatures?	*Rats*
9 Which famous abbey is depicted on the Bayeux Tapestry?	*Westminster Abbey*
10 Which film about the young Bard of Avon was nominated for 13 Oscars in 1999?	Shakespeare In Love

Quiz 117
Question 4

Quiz 117
Question 5

Quiz 119

FOOD AND DRINK

Questions	Answers
1 According to tradition, what is the significance of finding a coin in a Christmas pudding?	*It symbolizes future wealth*
2 Ananas is the alternative name of which fruit?	*Pineapple*
3 In Germany it is traditional to hide which food item in a Christmas tree?	*A pickle*
4 The name of which soup, when translated into English, means 'pepper water'?	*Mulligatawny*
5 What name is given to rubbing butter or oil into a turkey's skin to help with browning?	*Basting*
6 Which kind of fruit is a mirabelle?	*Plum*
7 What is the epicarp of an orange?	*The peel*
8 What does the word *trocken* mean on a German wine bottle?	*Dry*
9 How is candy floss known in the USA?	*Cotton candy*
10 Did Louis Pasteur invent the pasteurization process in the 18th or 19th century?	*19th century*

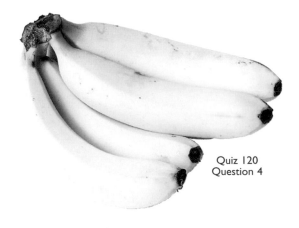

Quiz 120
Question 4

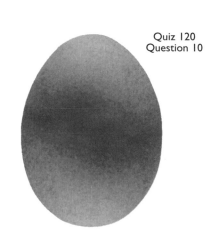

Quiz 120
Question 10

Quiz 120
FOOD AND DRINK

Questions	Answers
1 What is the significance of finding a ring in a Christmas pudding?	*It signifies a forth-coming marriage*
2 What is the main ingredient of the Greek dish taramasalata?	*Fish roe (eggs)*
3 In Poland, the Christmas Eve feast comprises 12 different dishes representing what?	*The 12 months of the year*
4 What type of fruit is a plantain?	*Banana*
5 What is the Italian word for pie?	*Pizza*
6 What type of pastry is used to make profiteroles?	*Choux pastry*
7 What is the dish of stuffed vine leaves called?	*Dolmas*
8 Which dessert of meringue, cream and fruit was named after a Russian ballerina?	*Pavlova*
9 What is ghee?	*Clarified butter*
10 Albumen is the technical name for what?	*White of an egg*

Quiz 119
Question 6

Quiz 119
Question 2

Quiz 121
GENERAL KNOWLEDGE

Questions	Answers
1 Where, according to the film title, did Marty McFly go?	Back to the Future
2 In 1983, who became the first American woman in space?	*Sally Ride*
3 How many grand slam tournaments are there in tennis?	*Four*
4 Which fruit would you be eating if ordering *pamplemousse* at a French restaurant?	*Grapefruit*
5 What is the longest side of a right-angled triangle called?	*Hypotenuse*
6 Which pianist joined the Chicago Symphony Orchestra when he was just nine years old?	*Liberace*
7 What type of creature is Norbert in the *Harry Potter* novels?	*Dragon*
8 To which fish family do goldfish belong?	*Carp*
9 Which pop singer was desperately seeking Susan on film?	*Madonna*
10 Which cartoon canine often referred to his adversary as a cotton-picking muskrat?	*Deputy Dawg*

Quiz 122
Question 6

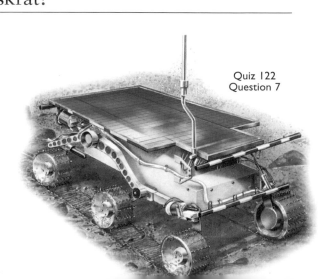

Quiz 122
Question 7

Quiz 122

GENERAL KNOWLEDGE

Questions	Answers
1 Who played the spy Harry Palmer in three films?	Michael Caine
2 In which city is Checkpoint Charlie Museum?	Berlin
3 What is the name of John Lennon's oldest son?	Julian Lennon
4 What is the only American state beginning with the letter P?	Pennsylvania
5 "Food Glorious Food" is a song from which Oscar-winning musical?	Oliver
6 In which building did Prince Charles and Lady Diana Spencer marry?	St Paul's Cathedral
7 The American space probe, *Pathfinder*, carried what to Mars in 1997?	Sojourner, *a small rover*
8 1996 was the Chinese year of which rodent?	The rat
9 Which is the only American city that is home to a royal palace?	Honolulu
10 Which Belgian cartoon character was 70 years old in 1999?	Tintin

Quiz 121
Question 4

Quiz 121
Question 7

Quiz 121
Question 9

Quiz 123
SCIENCE AND MATHS

Questions	Answers
1 What type of blood cells are responsible for transporting oxygen around the body?	*Red blood cells*
2 The renal artery supplies blood to which organ?	*Kidney*
3 What is the opposite of estivation?	*Hibernation*
4 How many furlongs are there in 12 miles?	*96 (12 x 8)*
5 Which element is the most toxic substance known to man?	*Plutonium*
6 Name the old measurement that was taken from the tip of the middle finger to the elbow?	*Cubit*
7 Which element has the lowest boiling point?	*Helium*
8 If an isosceles triangle has two angles of 70 degrees, what does the third angle measure?	*40 degrees*
9 What is the square root of 121?	*11*
10 What are helium, neon, xenon, krypton and radon?	*Noble gasses*

Quiz 124
Question 5

Quiz 124
SCIENCE AND MATHS

Questions	Answers
1 What is the name of the branch of mechanics that deals with the motion and action of forces?	*Dynamics*
2 What name is given to the time of year, when night and day are of equal lengths?	*Equinox*
3 A supermarket sold 72 oranges from its stock of 96. What percentage did it sell?	*75 percent*
4 In the human body where would you find an oval window and a round window?	*In the ear*
5 In June 1965 astronaut Edward H. White II, became the first American to do what?	*Walk in space*
6 What is the medical name for the breastbone?	*Sternum*
7 What is the cube root of 343?	*Seven* *(7 x 7 x 7 = 343)*
8 What machines have ROM and RAM?	*Computers*
9 What are there 10,080 of in a week?	*Minutes*
10 How many feet are there in a mile?	*5280*

Quiz 123
Question 2

Quiz 125
GENERAL KNOWLEDGE

Questions	Answers
1 Which festive song composed by Johnny Marks, was based on a poem by Robert L May?	**"Rudolph the Red-Nosed Reindeer"**
2 In which country would you find Mount Vesuvius?	*Italy*
3 Which precious gem is also the name given to a baseball pitch?	*Diamond*
4 Which Senator ran in opposition to George W Bush in the 2004 Presidential Elections?	*John F Kerry*
5 Charon is a moon of which planet?	*Pluto*
6 K1, K2, C1 and C2 are all categories in which sport?	*Canoeing*
7 Which 1997 film starring Robin Williams was a remake of the *Absent-Minded Professor*?	**Flubber**
8 What is the central bank of the US called?	*The Federal Reserve*
9 Alphabetically, what is the first sign of the zodiac?	*Aquarius*
10 Who connects the films *48 Hours* and *Down and Out in Beverly Hills*?	*Nick Nolte*

Quiz 126
Question 9

Quiz 126
Question 2

Quiz 126
GENERAL KNOWLEDGE

Questions	Answers
1 In the USA, which horse race is known as The Run for the Roses?	*Kentucky Derby*
2 What type of animal is a reebok?	*Wild deer or antelope*
3 For which song was Mary Poppins accompanied by a robin redbreast?	*"A Spoonful Of Sugar"*
4 The Balearic Islands belong to which European country?	*Spain*
5 Which ocean did the steamship *Savannah* cross in 1819?	**The Atlantic Ocean**
6 Which orchestral suite was completed by Gustav Holst in 1916?	**The Planet Suite**
7 Which is the bestselling doll in the world for girls?	*Barbie*
8 Which Disney film features the song "When I See An Elephant Fly"?	**Dumbo**
9 In which combat sport is a Grand Champion bestowed with the title of Yokozuma?	*Sumo wrestling*
10 Which US president was nicknamed 'Ten Cent Jimmy'?	*James Buchanan*

Quiz 125
Question 1

Quiz 127
SCIENCE AND MATHS

Questions	Answers
1 The Cambrian Period in history takes its name from discoveries in which country?	*Wales*
2 Which type of boat has underwater wings attached to the front and rear of its hull?	*Hydrofoil*
3 What does the diameter of a circle multiplied by pi equal?	*The circumference*
4 The duck-billed platypus and the spiny anteater are the only two mammals that do what?	*Lay eggs*
5 Guglielmo Marconi is associated with the development of what type of communication?	*Wireless telegraphy*
6 The Galapagos Islands are off the western coast of which continent?	*South America*
7 What kind of vehicle is a bathyscaphe?	*Submarine*
8 Where in the body is the tympanum?	*The ear (the eardrum)*
9 Which term describes half the diameter of a circle?	*The radius*
10 How many minutes are there in a day?	*1440*

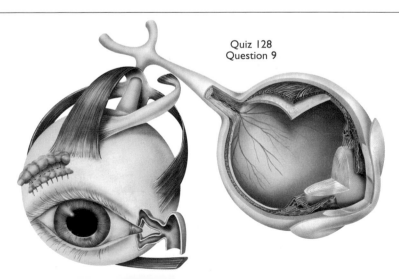

Quiz 128
Question 9

Quiz 128
GENERAL KNOWLEDGE

Questions	Answers
1 What is the lowest point on Earth?	*The Dead Sea*
2 At what temperature in centigrade does water boil?	*100 degrees*
3 Which classic novel is set in a house called Manderley?	**Rebecca**
4 Which sport was invented in 1891 by a Canadian minister called Dr James Naismith?	*Basketball*
5 What links the following: Ob, Orinoco, Okavango and Oder?	*They are all rivers*
6 What is the capital of Morocco?	*Rabat*
7 What is unusual about plants that are grown hydroponically?	*They are grown in water not soil*
8 How many hours are there in a fortnight?	*336*
9 Optometrists, ophthamologists and opticians are all concerned with what?	*Eyes (and vision)*
10 What type of animal is a sidewinder?	*Snake*

Quiz 127
Question 7

Quiz 127
Question 2

Quiz 129

GENERAL KNOWLEDGE

Questions	Answers
1 What is the average age of a group of children aged 13, 12, 10, 6 and 4?	*Nine*
2 What is an apiarist?	*Beekeeper*
3 Coal is made up mostly of which non-metallic element?	*Carbon*
4 Which is the world's largest desert?	*The Sahara*
5 What name is given to a frequency greater than that which can be heard by humans?	*Supersonic*
6 Gabriel Fahrenheit, inventor of a widely used temperature scale, came from which country?	*Germany*
7 Which planet has two moons named Deimos and Phobos?	*Mars*
8 How much is 35 percent of 300?	*105*
9 What do you call a cross between a horse and a donkey?	*Mule*
10 If a person is myopic, from what condition does he or she suffer?	*Near-sightedness*

Quiz 130
Question 4

Quiz 130
GENERAL KNOWLEDGE

Questions	Answers
1 What name is given to a female donkey?	*Jennet*
2 What term describes the air resistance that slows down aircraft?	*Drag*
3 Reduce $21/39$ to its simplest terms.	$7/13$
4 Zoology, a biological science, is the study of what?	*Animals*
5 Which type of coal is harder – bituminous or anthracite?	*Anthracite*
6 What do we call the process of shaping metal by hammering it while it is still hot?	*Forging*
7 Who invented the lightning rod?	*Benjamin Franklin*
8 A piano usually has how many keys?	*88*
9 Which is the odd one out: apple, tomato, pea pod, potato?	*Potato (the others are all fruit)*
10 Who first observed the moons of Jupiter?	*Galileo Galilei*

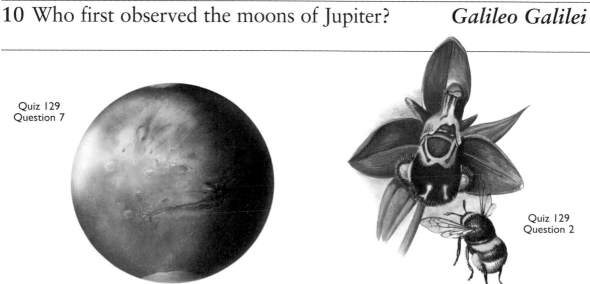

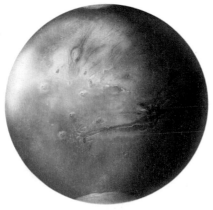

Quiz 129
Question 7

Quiz 129
Question 2

Quiz 131
THE BIBLE

Questions	Answers
1 What is the name of the Virgin Mary's mother?	Anne
2 What was the only miracle performed by Jesus that is mentioned in all four gospels?	The feeding of the five thousand
3 Which star led the three Wise Men to Jesus?	The star of Bethlehem
4 What is the longest book in the Bible?	The Book of Psalms
5 What religion did Mary and Joseph follow?	Judaism
6 At 969 years old, what is the name of the oldest person in the Bible?	Methuselah
7 Jesus grew up in Nazareth. In which modern-day country is Nazareth?	Israel
8 In which garden did Judas betray Jesus?	The Garden of Gethsemane
9 What was the first bird released by Noah from the ark?	Raven
10 What was written on two stone tablets and is also known as The Decalogue?	The Ten Commandments

Quiz 132
Question 2

Quiz 132
THE BIBLE

Questions	Answers
1 In which river did John the Baptist baptize Jesus?	*River Jordan*
2 According to the Bible, what was 300 cubits long and 15 cubits wide?	*Noah's ark*
3 Which 1999 Christmas hit for Cliff Richard was based on the Lord's Prayer?	*"The Millennium Prayer"*
4 Which religious group issues a magazine called *The Watch Tower*?	*Jehovah's Witnesses*
5 Whose wife was turned to a pillar of salt?	*Lot*
6 Who was the father of twin sons called Jacob and Esau?	*Isaac*
7 Which ruler did the three Wise Men talk with on their way to see Jesus?	*King Herod*
8 In which village did Jesus turn water into wine?	*Cana*
9 Which of the three Wise Men shares his name with a sixteen-size bottle of champagne?	*Balthazar*
10 In the Bible, what was the name of the tower that was built in an attempt to reach heaven?	*The Tower of Babel*

Quiz 131
Question 5

Quiz 131
Question 10

Quiz 133
GENERAL KNOWLEDGE

Questions	Answers
1 Bora, sirocco and mistral are all the names of what?	*Winds*
2 In the nursery rhyme, what does Jack jump over?	*The candlestick*
3 What nationality is the fashion designer Giorgio Armani?	*Italian*
4 Which black-and-white Antarctic bird can swim but not fly?	*Penguin*
5 Which Egyptian president was assassinated in 1981 whilst attending a military parade?	*Anwar Sadat*
6 Who played the wife of Dustin Hoffman in the film *Kramer vs. Kramer*?	*Meryl Streep*
7 Which was the first film based on a Shakespeare play to win the Best Film Oscar?	Hamlet
8 In *Star Trek*, which evil race of aliens armed themselves with sonic disrupter pistols?	*Klingons*
9 What French equivalent of the name Peter is also the state capital of South Dakota?	*Pierre*
10 What does the Greek drink *ouzo* taste of?	*Aniseed*

Quiz 134
Question 8

Quiz 134
Question 7

Quiz 134
GENERAL KNOWLEDGE

Questions	Answers
1 From what fruit is the syrup grenadine distilled?	*Pomegranate*
2 The fabric damask was named after which capital city?	*Damascus*
3 What is the tallest inhabited building in the US?	*Sears Tower*
4 The African city of Monrovia was named after which US president?	*James Monroe*
5 What metal was mined in stannaries?	*Tin*
6 In 1863, what explosive invention was patented by Alfred Nobel?	*Dynamite*
7 What does the drink *kahlua* taste of?	*Coffee*
8 What is Jupiter's largest moon?	*Ganymede*
9 The name of which car manufacturer is also the state capital of Texas?	*Austin*
10 Which two countries beginning with B form a land border with Argentina?	*Brazil and Bolivia*

Quiz 133
Question 2

Quiz 133
Question 4

Quiz 135
FOOD AND DRINK

Questions	Answers
1 What kind of pasta has a name that means 'little worms'?	*Vermicelli*
2 What is the country of origin of Parmesan cheese?	*Italy*
3 What is crossed with a tangerine to make an ugli fruit?	*Grapefruit*
4 Which Italian bread, made with olive oil, has a name that literally means 'slipper'?	*Ciabatta*
5 Tokay wine originates from which European country?	*Hungary*
6 What type of whisky is distilled from barley?	*Malt whisky*
7 Which country produces an oatmeal-covered cheese called Cabot?	*Scotland*
8 Calvados brandy is distilled from which fruit?	*Apples*
9 From which bird is pâté de foie gras obtained?	*Goose*
10 Which fungus makes bread rise?	*Yeast*

Quiz 136
Question 1

Quiz 136
Question 6

Quiz 136
FOOD AND DRINK

Questions	Answers
1 What type of fish is a kipper?	*A herring*
2 What is added to champagne to make a champagne flip?	*The yolk of an egg*
3 In which US state is the Napa Valley wine producing area?	*California*
4 Which salad was named after the American hotel where it was first made?	*Waldorf salad*
5 What name is given to the cocktail of gin, vermouth and orange?	*Bronx*
6 Which herb is used to make pesto sauce?	*Basil*
7 From where in the world does the hot sauce harissa originate?	*North Africa*
8 Which Portuguese city gave its name to the drink called port?	*Oporto*
9 Chianti wine originated in which country?	*Italy*
10 If a dish is described as à la Brettonne, what is it garnished with?	*Beans*

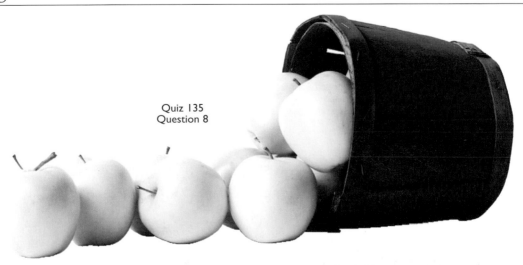

Quiz 135
Question 8

Quiz 137
GENERAL KNOWLEDGE

Questions	Answers
1 The Eurasia Basin is the deepest point in which ocean?	*Arctic Ocean*
2 Which manic comic actor played the title role in the 1996 film *The Cable Guy*?	*Jim Carrey*
3 The word *Sverige* is inscribed on the stamps of which North European country?	*Sweden*
4 In Japan, a *sensei* is a teacher of what?	*Martial arts*
5 Who did Sylvester Stallone play in the film *First Blood*?	*John Rambo*
6 In which Australian state is Ayers Rock?	*Northern Territories*
7 Which comet orbits the Sun every 76 years?	*Halley's comet*
8 Which planet is the closest in size to the Earth?	*Venus*
9 Which Egyptian city is the only African city that has an underground railway system?	*Cairo*
10 In the legend, what did Arthur pull from the stone to become king?	*A sword*

Quiz 138
Question 3

Quiz 138
Question 7

Quiz 138
GENERAL KNOWLEDGE

Questions	Answers
1 Which European capital city is served by Orly Airport?	*Paris*
2 On whose stories was the Disney film *The Jungle Book* based?	*Rudyard Kipling's*
3 In the fairytale, what does the ugly duckling become?	*A swan*
4 In which US desert does Death Valley lie?	**Mojave Desert**
5 Which form of carbon is the main constituent of pencil lead?	*Graphite*
6 In which Oscar-winning film did Kevin Costner play Lieutenant John Dunbar?	**Dances With Wolves**
7 What accompanies bacon in the dish angels-on-horseback?	*Oysters*
8 What is the largest lake in North America?	*Lake Superior*
9 In which Asian mountain range is the yeti said to live?	*Himalayas*
10 What is our galaxy called?	*The Milky Way*

Quiz 137
Question 10

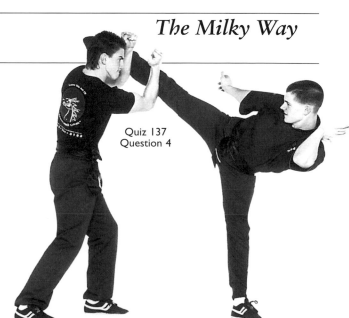

Quiz 137
Question 4

Quiz 139
NATURAL WORLD

Questions	Answers
1 Which is the only bird from which leather is obtained?	*Ostrich*
2 Which horned animals congregate in a group called a crash?	*Rhinos*
3 The okapi is a close relative of which animal?	*Giraffe*
4 Which of the following is a pachyderm: a worm, an elephant or a whale?	*Elephant*
5 What is the more common name for the vibrissae of a cat?	*Whiskers*
6 What five-letter name is given to the tail of a fox?	*Brush*
7 What type of falcon was also the name of King Arthur's wizard?	*Merlin*
8 Which animal, native to South America, is the world's largest rodent?	*The capybara*
9 What is the smallest breed of horse?	*Falabella*
10 What are the tusks of a walrus made of?	*Ivory*

Quiz 140
Question 7

Quiz 140
Question 2

Quiz **140**
NATURAL WORLD

Questions	Answers
1 Which animal lives in a holt?	*Otter*
2 Which is the official national animal of Canada?	*Beaver*
3 What is a gila monster?	*Poisonous lizard*
4 Is a jackal a feline or a canine?	*Canine*
5 What is the alternative four-letter name for a cougar?	*Puma*
6 What name is given to a male adult seal?	*Bull*
7 Brown and rainbow are both varieties of which freshwater fish?	*Trout*
8 What do the Red Data Books provide a list of?	*Endangered species*
9 What is a terrapin?	*A freshwater turtle*
10 How many toes does a rhinoceros have?	*Twelve, three on each foot*

Quiz 139
Question 2

Quiz 139
Question 8

Quiz 141
GENERAL KNOWLEDGE

Questions	Answers
1 The adjective lupine describes which animal?	Wolf
2 What type of animal is a gharial?	Crocodile
3 Which Simon and Garfunkel hit begins "A winter's day in a deep and dark December"?	"I Am A Rock"
4 Wolfram is an old name for which chemical element?	Tungsten
5 Which actor shot John Travolta in Pulp Fiction?	Bruce Willis
6 Black bottom, gavotte and quadrille are all the names of what?	Dances
7 Which stage musical featured the song "The Movie In My Mind" and was set in Vietnam?	Miss Saigon
8 Name the famous pirate from J M Barrie's fantasy Peter Pan.	Captain Hook
9 What are the names of Harry Potter's parents?	Lily and James
10 Kobe Bryant, Magic Johnson and Wilt Chamberlain all played which sport?	Basketball

Quiz 142
Question 7

Quiz 142
GENERAL KNOWLEDGE

Questions	Answers
1 In which 1971 film did Topol sing "If I Were A Rich Man"?	Fiddler on the Roof
2 Which large musical instrument is also known as a bull fiddle?	*Double bass*
3 What was the nationality of car manufacturer Ferdinand Porsche?	*Austrian*
4 In the Bible, what name is given to the battle that signifies the end of the world?	*Armageddon*
5 What type of fork was invented by trumpet player John Shore in 1711?	*Tuning fork*
6 Which album entered the US album chart in 1973 and didn't leave again until 1988?	**Dark Side of the Moon** (*Pink Floyd*)
7 What is the name of the area of the North Pole where the soil is permanently frozen?	*Tundra*
8 What name is given to the dead skin around the base of a finger or toenail?	*Cuticle*
9 In which US state do citizens sunbathe on the Waikiki beach?	*Hawaii*
10 Which element discovered in 1898 is associated with Superman?	*Krypton*

Quiz 141
Question 8

Quiz 141
Question 2

Quiz 143
SCIENCE AND MATHS

Questions	Answers
1 In which gland of the human body is iodine stored?	*Thyroid gland*
2 Which two planets have no known moons?	*Mercury and Venus*
3 A microchip is constructed on a single piece of what?	*Silicon*
4 A rectangular garden has a perimeter of 40 m. If the garden is 8 m wide, how long is it?	*12 m*
5 Which three planets are not visible to the naked eye?	*Uranus, Neptune and Pluto*
6 Anton van Leeuwenhoek was credited with developing the first what?	*Microscope*
7 Which metallic elements are most common in meteorites?	*Iron and nickel*
8 Divide two gross by a dozen.	*24 (2 x 144 ÷ 12)*
9 Where would you find the Crest of Ilium?	*The hip bone*
10 What do you do if you boot up a computer?	*Start it*

Quiz 144
Question 6

Questions	Answers
1 To the nearest whole number, how many times weaker is the Moon's gravity than the Earth's?	*Six*
2 Write or say this number in figures: nine and three-quarter million.	*9,750,000*
3 What did Sir Isaac Newton define as an object's mass multiplied by its velocity?	*Its momentum*
4 Which muscle contracts to straighten your arm?	*The triceps*
5 What is the process that kills disease-producing micro-organisms in food and drink by heat?	*Pasteurization*
6 A neurologist specializes in which area of science?	*The human nervous system*
7 What does humidity measure?	*The amount of water in the air*
8 What process converts petroleum, or crude oil, into usable fuels?	*Refining*
9 A lighthouse beam flashes every 12 seconds. How many times will it flash in a day?	*7200*
10 What is the common name for grape sugar?	*Glucose*

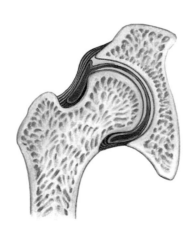

Quiz 143
Question 9

Quiz 143
Question 6

Quiz 145
GENERAL KNOWLEDGE

Questions	Answers
1 To which animal does the adjective porcine apply?	*Pig*
2 What is the better-known name of The Church Of Jesus Christ Of Latter Day Saints?	*The Mormons*
3 In the nursery rhyme, who came to town riding on a pony with a feather in his cap?	*Yankee Doodle Dandy*
4 Where in the human body are the bones called the carpals?	*The wrist*
5 Which country is Beirut the capital of?	*Lebanon*
6 Leopard and Weddell are both species of which animal?	*Seal*
7 Which officer training school for the US Army was founded in 1802?	*West Point*
8 Which vowel is denoted by two dots in Morse Code?	*I*
9 What is Tiger Wood's real name?	*Eldrick*
10 Who is known as the Vicar of Christ?	*The Pope*

Quiz 146
Question 10

Quiz 146
Question 1

Quiz 146
Question 2

Quiz 146
GENERAL KNOWLEDGE

Questions	Answers
1 Arch, girder and suspension are all types of which construction?	*Bridge*
2 What is a mudpuppy?	*A type of salamander*
3 What is the seed-bearing organ of a flower called?	*Pistil*
4 Where is your thyroid?	*In your neck*
5 Which 2001 film told the true story of the mathematician John Nash?	**A Beautiful Mind**
6 Which American composer wrote "Rhapsody in Blue"?	*George Gershwin*
7 Who wrote the poems *Paradise Lost* and *Paradise Regained*?	*John Milton*
8 In which US state is Long Beach Airport?	*California*
9 Which country has the world's largest army?	*China*
10 In 1955, which legendary actor died whilst making the film *Giant*?	*James Dean*

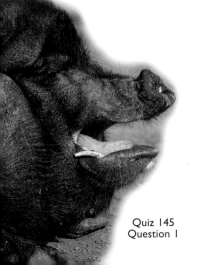

Quiz 145
Question 1

Quiz 145
Question 6

Quiz 147
GEOGRAPHY

Questions	Answers
1 What is the name of the sea that separates Greece from Turkey?	*Aegean Sea*
2 Which river flows from Lake Tanganyika to the Mediterranean Sea?	*The Nile*
3 Which sea is linked to the Mediterranean Sea by the Suez Canal?	*Red Sea*
4 The source of which river lies in the Valdai Hills near the city of Moscow?	*The Volga*
5 Which windy city is on the shore of Lake Michigan?	*Chicago*
6 What is the capital of the Canadian province Alberta?	*Edmonton*
7 The German capital of Berlin lies on which river?	*The Spree*
8 Which country produces the most gold?	*South Africa*
9 Which spectacular waterfall is located on the borders of Argentina and Brazil?	*Iguaçu Falls*
10 Which river has its source in the Black Forest and empties into the Black Sea?	*The Danube*

Quiz 148
Question 8

Quiz 148
GEOGRAPHY

Questions	Answers
1 In which ocean are the Maldives?	*Indian Ocean*
2 What is the name of the trench that is the deepest point of the Pacific Ocean?	*Marianas Trench*
3 Which sea lies between New Zealand and Australia?	*Tasman Sea*
4 The Colorado River runs through which US canyon?	*The Grand Canyon*
5 Which is the longest river in South America?	*The Amazon*
6 On which river does the city of Buenos Aires stand?	*Rio de la Plata*
7 Opened in 1822, which canal links the east and west coast of Scotland?	*Caledonian Canal*
8 Which is the longest river in North America?	*The Mississippi*
9 Which river is overlooked by the Leaning Tower of Pisa?	*The Arno*
10 How was Lake Tiberias otherwise known in the Bible?	*The Sea of Galilee*

Quiz 147
Question 5

Quiz 149
GENERAL KNOWLEDGE

Questions	Answers
1 Which TV family owned a pet dragon called Spot?	*The Munsters*
2 How many bottles of champagne does a jeroboam hold?	*Four*
3 What word is used to describe a person who has been appointed to vote in place of another?	*Proxy*
4 Is alligator or crocodile the Spanish word for lizard?	*Alligator*
5 Who sang "Wandrin' Star" in the film *Paint Your Wagon*?	*Lee Marvin*
6 Appaloosa and Arab are both breeds of which animal?	*Horse*
7 What is the state capital of West Virginia, which gave its name to a dance?	*Charleston*
8 What type of animal is Fozzie in *The Muppet Show*?	*Bear*
9 The *Titanic* was launched from which Irish city?	*Belfast*
10 Who was Bob Hope's male co-star in seven road movies?	*Bing Crosby*

Quiz 150
Question 7

Quiz 150
Question 5

Quiz 150
GENERAL KNOWLEDGE

Questions	Answers
1 Which US university administers the Pulitzer Prizes?	*Columbia University*
2 Who is the sister of Joan Collins, who wrote the novel *Hollywood Wives*?	*Jackie Collins*
3 What are both the Julian and the Gregorian?	*Types of calendar*
4 In the US, what was the former name of the Hoover Dam?	*Boulder Dam*
5 What type of animal is Robin in *The Muppet Show*?	*Frog*
6 In World War II, when did D Day occur?	*6 June, 1944*
7 Brian Trubshaw was the first test pilot of which famous plane?	*Concorde*
8 Which organization has an emblem of a candle surrounded by barbed wire?	*Amnesty International*
9 Which film starring Burt Reynolds featured a race from Connecticut to California?	**The Cannonball Run**
10 To a sailor, what is *mal de mer*?	*Seasickness*

Quiz 149
Question 8

Quiz 151
HISTORY

Questions	Answers
1 Which lost Inca city was rediscovered by Hiram Bingham in 1911?	*Machu Picchu*
2 Which country was ruled by Ivan the Terrible?	*Russia*
3 Who was the first woman to fly solo across the Atlantic?	*Amelia Earhart*
4 Who replaced Gray Davis as governor of California in November 2003?	*Arnold Schwarzenegger*
5 Which Norwegian adventurer sailed the Pacific on a balsawood raft?	*Thor Heyerdahl*
6 What was the name of the short arrow shot from a crossbow?	*A bolt, or 'quarrel'*
7 Which Scottish leader defeated the English at Bannockburn in 1314?	*Robert the Bruce*
8 In the First World War, what was 'No Man's Land'?	*Area between the trenches*
9 Which San Franciscan bridge was completed in 1937 and spans 1280 m?	*Golden Gate Bridge*
10 Which Italian Renaissance artist had the surname Buonarroti?	*Michelangelo*

Quiz 152
Question 3